DOWS

Born in Malawi and educated at schools
in Africa and England, Tom Williamson
read geology at Brasenose College,
Oxford. After a further degree in geochemistry at the University of Leeds, he
worked for a period in Africa as a field
geologist. He then spent a number of
years on the staff of the Science Museum,
London, specializing in climatology and
the history of medicine. Tom Williamson
has written many articles on dowsing
research and two earth science books for
children. He is married and lives in
Dorset.

DOWSING

New Light on an Ancient Art

TOM WILLIAMSON

ROBERT HALE · LONDON

© Tom Williamson 1993
First published in Great Britain 1993
Paperback edition 2002

ISBN 0 7090 7098 5

Robert Hale Limited
Clerkenwell House
Clerkenwell Green
London EC1R 0HT

Printed in Great Britain by
St Edmundsbury Press Limited,
Bury St Edmunds, Suffolk and bound by
Woolnough Bookbinding Limited, Irthlingborough

Contents

They tell us something strange and odd,
About a certain magic rod,
That, bending down its top, divines
Whene'er the soil has golden mines

Virtues of Sid Hamlet the Magician's Rod
Jonathan Swift (1710)

Illustrations

PICTURE CREDITS

Illustration section
Science Museum Library: 1. British Library: 2, 3, 6, 7.
M. Biezanski: 8. H-D Betz: 15. S. Williamson: 13, 14.

Textual Diagrams
H-D Betz: fig. 2. D.G. Chadwick: fig. 4.

Acknowledgements

This book has been long in gestation and over the years many people have contributed towards it, not least my wife Sara Swee Yong through her patience and support. In researching the history of dowsing, I have benefited from the published work of Christopher Bird as well as the helpful staff of the British Library. I am grateful to the University of Chicago Press for permission to quote passages from *Water Witching USA* by Evon Vogt and Ray Hyman, and to Bloomsbury Publishers for permission to quote an extract from Peter Redgrove's *The Black Goddess and the Sixth Sense*.

Amongst dowsers, I am first of all grateful to my father, the late Andrew Williamson, whose meticulous reports on dowsing for water in the volcanic and crystalline rocks of East Africa remain of lasting scientific value. The late Colonel A.H. Bell, DSO, OBE, founder and first President of the British Society of Dowsers, contributed substantially to this East African project. I am also indebted to two even more experienced dowsers: geophysicist Andrei Apostol, of New York City and engineer Hans Schröter, currently dowsing for desperately needed water in Namibia, southern Africa.

Andrei Apostol has provided much invaluable information and ideas concerning dowsing in Romania, theories of dowsing and many other topics. Hans Schröter, regarded by *cognoscenti* as the world's most accomplished dowser, has kindly allowed me to report in detail both on his worldwide dowsing activities and his impressive performance in scientific tests.

Hans Schröter and Andrei Apostol were two of the many dowsers who participated in the recent government-funded investigation of dowsing in Germany. For background information on this important project and other matters I am much obliged to Professor Dr Hans-Dieter Betz, of the Physics Department in Ludwig-Maximilians-Universität, Munich. Other scientists who have over the years supplied facts and ideas for Part I of the book include the late Dr Solco Tromp, geologist and biometeorologist, of Leiden, the Netherlands; Professor Duane Chadwick, of the College of Engineering, Utah State University and Dr Robin Baker, of the Department of Zoology at the University of Manchester. Professor Richard Bailey of the University of Newcastle-upon-Tyne kindly provided many helpful details concerning dowsing and church archaeology.

My thanks are due to oil geologists Coleman Morton, of Pasadena, California and Richard Barca, of Jackson, Michigan for information on dowsing in relation to geological structure in the USA.

I am specially indebted to the late Professor Yves Rocard, CBE, Grand Officier of the Legion of Honour and one time Director of the Physics Laboratory in the Ecole Normale Supérieure in Paris, for stimulating discussions and a continuous stream of ideas on how dowsers may respond to magnetic fields. Rocard, who was much ridiculed for his belief that the human body and brain contain millions of minute magnetite crystals, died at the age of 88 on 16 March 1992. Two months later, a group of scientists at Caltech announced their discovery of millions of minute magnetite crystals in the human brain.

Introduction

Challenge to Science

Can someone walking along holding a forked stick – a dowser – really find mineral veins, water, or other things hidden underground? Can some dowsers actually detect harmful rays rising from below or even mysterious Earth forces perhaps known to the builders of Stonehenge and other stone circles? And what about crop circle dowsing? Can we really believe those dowsers who say they can detect strange forces associated with these enigmatic markings that have in recent years been discovered in crops around the world?

Fifteen years ago, scientists would have answered all such questions with an almost unanimous 'No'. To quote two leading scientific authorities on dowsing:

> We don't have to resort to prejudice to dismiss water witching (dowsing) as invalid. The evidence for it, when assembled and examined is not merely insufficient ... it is appallingly negative. We know of few other hypotheses that have been put forth so persistently over such a long span of years with such consistently negative experimental findings as the hypothesis that water witching 'works'.[1]

But much has happened since those dismissive words were written. Dowsing has been used with impressive results not only by geologists in the former Soviet Union and Eastern Europe, but also by Western organizations as astute as the official German international aid agency, the GTZ. There have been astonishing advances in solving scientific mysteries akin to dowsing – for example how animals find their way without using conventional senses. And medical authorities have had to acknowledge that not only dowsers, but all of us can be affected by unseen noxious influences from below.

Most importantly of all, a group of highly respected scientists have at last tackled the problem of dowsing head on. Applying the most up-to-date scientific protocols, techniques and equipment, they have made discoveries that are crucial to a solution of the 500-year-old mystery.

Because these developments are either still at an early stage, or too recent to have been digested by the scientific community, their significance for dowsing has not yet been widely appreciated. Yet, as this book seeks to show, they have revolutionary implications for our understanding of the ancient art.

The emerging picture of dowsing is still, inevitably, rather blurred. But, as we shall see, what seems to be taking shape before our eyes is not just a scientific explanation of dowsing, but a whole new conception of our relationship with the Earth and its energy flows. The dowsers' response, is, it seems, only one of several hitherto mysterious effects which we can now begin to understand in terms of our sensitivity to several invisible but nonetheless real Earth influences or energies.

The resulting picture has certain parallels with the claims of some in the New Age movement and suggests that scientists would be unwise to dismiss all New Age ideas concerning the Earth. While there is certainly plenty of dross there, we will also find the occasional nugget of gold.

A remarkable feature of this new view of dowsing and related effects is that what seem to be novel discoveries turn out to have been anticipated in the folklore and mining culture of past centuries. The history of dowsing is therefore not only a fascinating story in its own right, it contains – as we shall see – much that is relevant to us today.

To their credit, the philosophers and scientists of those early days did not dismiss all this folk wisdom. It was not until the dawn of the Age of Reason in the eighteenth century that, with rare exceptions, intellectuals felt it beneath their dignity to discuss the ancient art of searching for minerals or water with a forked twig.

This development had an unfortunate effect on dowsing practice. Cut off from the oxygen of reasoned debate, some dowsers started to embellish their performance by not only claiming to find minerals and water, but also to divine depth, water yield, quality and many other things. To do this, they resurrected the old Roman diviner's pendulum. Just as the superstitious Romans had done, the modern diviners interpreted the handheld pendulum's movements as answers to whatever questions they asked.

Divination, usually with a pendulum, but sometimes by means of a rod, is now even more popular than it was in Roman times. Whatever the merits or otherwise of the practice, it is certainly not dowsing. For true dowsers, whether they are searching for minerals, water, oil, archaeological remains or even mysterious Earth energies allegedly emitted by ley lines, are united by one belief. They feel they are sensing some real change in the environment as they walk along.

To get a feel for this dowsing experience, why not try some experiments for yourself. There are two dowsing instruments to experiment with: the traditional forked rod or twig ('V' rod) and the pair of angle rods ('L' rods).

The traditional dowser's rod was a forked twig of hazel and some dowsers still prefer to use such rods today. But twigs from other trees such as willow and hawthorn, while lacking the springiness and lasting qualities of hazel, will also serve. Alternatively you could make a forked rod for yourself by taking two lengths, 20 to 30 centimetres long, of a suitably springy material such as nylon and then fasten them together at one end. I have made many such rods of fibre-reinforced plastic.

Now, hold the free ends of the rods in your hands, palms up, and keeping your elbows into your sides walk along. Try dowsing in various places with the rods. You may feel nothing at all. On the other hand, if the rods are of the right springiness and you have applied the right tension the rods may suddenly twist in your hands. This is the fundamental dowsing experience.

As an alternative to the forked stick, you can use a pair of 'L' rods. You can easily make these by cutting and bending an ordinary wire coat-hanger. Use the long bottom part of the coat-hanger as the long arm of the L and about 12 centimetres of one of the coat-hanger sides as the short arm. Then, with your elbows to your sides and holding the shorter arm of the L in your hands, walk along in such a way that the long arms are parallel and point directly ahead of you. You may find that the rods sometimes swing together or away from each other. This movement, caused by a slight twisting of your wrists, is the equivalent of the sudden flipping of the traditional 'V' rod.

Finally, there is the handheld pendulum. Although tradition-ally used by diviners to answer questions, a few people use pendulums, especially very long ones, for true dowsing. A great variety of cheap pendulums are on the market, but it is very easy to make one of your own by suspending any small object, such as a key ring, from a length of thread and letting it swing. To dowse with a pendulum, first hold the thread in one hand at a suitable point, letting the pendulum swing until it oscillates or gyrates constantly, and then walk along. At some point the pendulum may change its behaviour – for example, instead of oscillating, it may start to rotate. This, pendulum users claim, is a true dowsing response.

Having had a taste of dowsing, particularly if one has experienced the sudden flip of the traditional 'V' rod, it is easy to see why so much of the centuries-old debate has been conducted at an emotional rather than a rational level. Dowsers feel that something important is happening when the rod twitches in their hands, but they cannot explain exactly what. Equally, sceptics feel certain that such a ludicrous and unscientific procedure could not possibly be a sound way of detecting something hidden beneath the Earth's surface.

In fact, dowsers and their critics have devoted so much attention to the dowsing response that they often seem to have overlooked the crucial question – can dowsers really detect things underground? To answer that we can do no better than start at the beginning and relate the strange story of the dowsers, what they have sought, and what they have actually found.

Part One

1   The Ancient Art

It all seems to have started in Germany. Though the citizens of
the Roman Empire practised many forms of divination, dowsing
was unknown to them. The earliest references to true dowsing
come from the German-speaking lands of northern Europe in
the fifteenth century.[1] Once discovered, the art spread rapidly
and by the sixteenth century, miners in several parts of
Germany were using the technique to locate veins of metal ore.

Georg Bauer (1494–1555), the great Saxon-born pioneer of
mineralogy more commonly known as Georgius Agricola,
described how dowsers searched for ore in his famous work *De
Re Metallica*.[2] He wrote:

> All alike grasp the forks of the twig with their hands, clenching
> their fists, it being necessary that the clenched fingers should be
> held towards the sky in order that the twig should be raised at
> that end where the two branches meet. Then they wander hither
> and thither at random through mountainous regions. It is said
> that the moment they place their feet on a vein the twig
> immediately turns and twists and so by its action discloses the
> vein; when they move their feet again and go away from that spot
> the twig becomes once more immobile.

Agricola's account leaves little doubt that the German miners
were practising true dowsing, the apparent detection of things
underground. But the technique was still linked with divination,
or so Agricola believed, for he commented, 'The application of
the inchanted or divining rod to metallic matters took its rise
from magicians and the impure fountains of inchantment.'

For Agricola – as for many modern scientists – dowsing's past
links with the occult led him to view the technique with distrust.
He concluded, 'A miner, since we think he ought to be a good
and serious man, should not make use of an inchanted twig,
because if he is prudent and skilled in the natural signs, he
understands that a forked stick is no use to him.'

Despite Agricola's admonition, however, miners throughout
Germany continued to dowse for veins of metal ore. In the Harz
Mountains of northern Germany, miners used the technique for

hundreds of years to locate veins of silver, gold, copper, and iron. In the Rammelsberg Mountains, dowsers searched for lodes of silver, copper, iron and lead. In the Erzgebirge or Ore Mountains, now on the borders between Germany and Czechoslovakia, where Agricola himself learned the mining and metallurgical trades, many generations of miners used dowsing to help them find gold, lead, silver, copper and tungsten.

Dowsing soon spread beyond Germany. The growing manufacturing industries of the sixteenth and seventeenth centuries demanded more and more copper, lead, zinc and tin. So all over Europe, as mines expanded their operations, prospectors, including dowsers, travelled far and wide in their search for new deposits of metal ore.

In England, Elizabeth I encouraged German prospectors and mining experts to develop the resources of her island realm. Together with their expertise in smelting and metal-working the Germans also brought their art of searching for metal ores with a forked twig.

One part of England that benefited from German mining expertise was the county of Somerset. By the mid-seventeenth century, miners in the local Mendip Hills were using the rod to help find veins of lead and zinc ore and the practice came to the attention of Robert Boyle (1627–1691), one of the founding fathers of modern science. Boyle was intrigued and reported:

> one Gentleman, who lives near the Lead Mines in Somersetshire, leading me over those parts of the Mines where we knew that Metalline Veins did run, made me take note of the stooping of the Wand when he passed over a Vein of Oar, and protested that the motion of his hand did not at all contribute to the indications of the Wand, but that sometimes when he held it very fast, it would bend so strongly as to break in his hand. And to convince me that he believed himself, he did upon the promises made by the stooping Wand put himself to the great charge of digging in untryed places for Mines (but with what success he has not yet informed me). Among the miners themselves I found that some made use of the Wand and others laughed at it.[3]

Interestingly, miners in the Mendip Hills may have been the first people to use the word 'dowsing'. In 1692 John Locke (1632–1704) the famed Somerset philosopher, referred to the alleged ability of the 'deusing-rod' to discover mines of gold and silver.[4] Evidently the philosopher had heard local miners use their own word for the twig known to the Germans as the wishing rod or *Wünschelrute*.

The German miners introduced dowsing to another county in south-west England, Cornwall. Here the technique seems to have been admirably suited to local conditions, for by the eighteenth century, when Cornwall led the world in the production of tin and copper, Cornishmen had developed dowsing into an advanced prospecting technique.

In order to appreciate the sophistication of Cornish mine dowsing, we need to know something of the geology of the south-west peninsula of England. Anyone who has visited this region will have seen the rugged grey granite tors that form the backbone of the peninsula, stretching from Dartmoor in the east to Land's End in the west. The tors and the surrounding moorland are actually the top parts of a single immense mass of granite.

About 300 million years ago the molten granite rose from deep in the Earth's crust, fracturing the surrounding older rocks as it did so. As the huge molten mass slowly cooled, hot metal-rich fluids escaped and deposited minerals in the faults and fractures. These steeply inclined cracks now filled with valuable ores of tin, copper and tungsten, together with less valuable minerals such as the appropriately named magnetic iron ore, lodestone, are known as lodes. They are often irregular, pinching out in places, sometimes dividing into two, or showing signs of rupture and displacement by later Earth movements.

When a miner could see lodes at the surface, it was easy enough for him to follow their course. But often, because of soil cover, there were no surface clues to the underground course of lodes. It was here that dowsing came into its own.

We are fortunate in having a detailed description of exactly how Cornish mine dowsers traced mineral lodes. William Pryce, of Redruth, the great authority on Cornish mining practice, included an account of contemporary mine dowsing in his 1778 work *Mineralogia Cornubiensis*.[5] It was written by his friend William Cookworthy, of Plymouth, a pioneering industrialist who had greatly improved the manufacture of English porcelain.

Cookworthy reported that local miners made their dowsing rods from a single forked twig of hazel or other wood between two and a half and three feet long. Alternatively, they used 'two separate shoots tied together, with some vegetable substance as packthread'. Then he went on to make one of the most penetrating observations on dowsing that has ever been written, 'A man ought to hold the rod with the same indifference and inattention to, or reasoning about it or its effects, as he holds a fishing rod or a walking stick.' For, according to Cookworthy, the rod 'constantly answers in the hands of peasants, women and children, who hold it simply without puzzling their minds with doubts or reasonings'. Later on in the book, we shall see the full significance of Cookworthy's remarks.

William Cookworthy advised young dowsers to gain experience over known lodes, such as those visible near the sea shore. Then he instructed the novice dowser:

> Walk steadily and slowly on with it [the rod]; and a person that hath been accustomed to carry it will meet a single repulsion and attraction, every three, four, or five yards, which must not be heeded, it being only from the water that is between every bed of Killas [slate], Grouan [soft granite] or other strata. When the holder approaches a Lode so near its semidiameter, the rod feels loose in the hands and is very sensibly repelled toward the face. If it is thrown back so far as to touch the hat, it must be brought forward to its usual elevation, when it will continue to be repelled till the foremost foot is over the edge of the Lode. But as soon as the foremost foot is beyond its limits, the attraction from the hindmost foot, which is still on the Lode, or else the repulsion on the other side, or both, throw the rod back toward the face. The distance from the point where the attraction begun, and where it ended, is the breadth of the Lode.

Cookworthy said that a good dowser could in this way discover all the features of concealed lodes: their changes in breadth, where they pinched out, and where they were displaced by cross-cutting fractures. He noted that dowsing was particularly useful for tracing lodes that were 'alive to grass' in other words that contained workable ore right up to the surface. He also recommended the technique for finding what geologists would now call fracture zones – belts of rock shattered by past Earth movements. Although they were not necessarily mineralized, miners found it much easier to drive their tunnels through these zones than through solid rocks.

Clearly, Cornish dowsers had developed their art into quite an elaborate technique by the eighteenth century. But did it really work? William Pryce certainly thought so, for he quoted numerous dowsing successes in the county. For instance, after the Reverend Henry Hawkins Tremayne had found some stream tin in a pond at Heligan, miners speculated that a lode might be found nearby. A dowser then located what he thought was a lode below ground, and the miners sank a shaft there. A lode was indeed found though unfortunately it did not contain enough tin to make mining profitable.

In two other instances, Pryce reported, miners sank shafts on dowsing evidence, one at St. Germains, another between Penzance and Newlyn. In both cases, lodes containing mundick – an old mining term for iron sulphides – were found.

Again, Pryce related, William Cookworthy managed to trace the course of a concealed lode near St. Austell. At one point Cookworthy declared that the lode had been squeezed to nothing; this was later confirmed to be correct by the local miners. On another occasion, Cookworthy traced a lode from a point inland to the cliff at St. Austell Down. There he found by dowsing that the lode 'had a horse in it', in other words, it had been split in two. Miners subsequently confirmed that this was indeed the case.

Pryce reported another dowsing feat. A certain Captain Ribeira had deserted the King of Spain's service in the reign of Queen Anne and had been rewarded with the post of Captain Commandant of the Plymouth garrison. Ribeira was a keen dowser and had by this means discovered a deposit of copper ore near Okehampton, in Devon. Later, a mine was started there which operated for some years.

Pryce and Cookworthy's detailed description of Cornish mine dowsing in the eighteenth century shows how highly the leading English mineralogists of the day regarded the technique. This respect was echoed throughout Europe. In the German mines, for instance, dowsers at this time enjoyed a standing that has never since been equalled. Officially, their status was higher than that of surveyors, and mine dowsers were expected to possess a professional diploma in dowsing.

Mineral lode dowsing was equally valued in other parts of the world where Europeans had settled. In the fabulously rich silver mines of the High Andes in South America, for instance, the Spanish mining authorities were using the technique to help locate the abundant lodes of silver ore that had made the region around Potosi the largest source of silver in the Western world. Alonzo Barba, the Potosi priest and mining expert, described a peculiar T-shaped rod of his own design which dowsers then used in the Potosi mines.[6]

How had mine dowsers achieved this surprising status? One reason, clearly, was a record of success good enough to impress hardnosed mine owners as well as technical experts like William Pryce. But success alone would not have been enough in an age when scientific thought was developing rapidly and causes were being sought for all phenomena. It seems likely that an equally important reason for dowsing's high standing was that it could be explained in terms of contemporary scientific ideas. Thus, before quoting Cookworthy's description of practical dowsing, Pryce gave a lengthy exposition of dowsing theory.

In fact, from the sixteenth century onwards, the bending of a forked twig over a hidden mineral vein had spawned theories in the same way as any other natural phenomenon. From the start, some sceptics had maintained that the dowsers moved the rod themselves and that this had nothing to do with the presence of mineral veins. But this would hardly explain the successes of the technique. So, quite reasonably, most of the theories assumed that the mineral vein emitted something that caused the dowsers' rod to flip. But what precisely was this invisible influence? How did it act? Did it affect the rod directly or merely cause the dowser to twist it? These were the questions that challenged some of the most distinguished thinkers of the time.

Several sages, influenced by the atomic theory of the ancient Greeks, believed that metallic atoms or corpuscles rose from the veins and interacted with the atoms of the rod, causing it to move. Among the supporters of this idea, were two eminent French savants, Pierre Gassendi (1592–1655), the first person to observe the transit of the planet Mercury across the face of the sun, and Nicolas Malebranche (1638–1715), the philosopher and clergyman. Malebranche's views on dowsing gained wide publicity as the result of an extraordinary story of crime and punishment.

The episode started on July 6 1692, when a wine merchant and his wife were found hacked to death in their house in Lyons. As a large amount of money was missing from a strongbox in the house, it seemed clear that robbery was the motive. But where were the villains? In desperation, the law officers sought the help of a dowser named Jacques Aymar Vernay, from the village of Saint Marcellin, in the Dauphiné region of France. Aymar claimed that his rod could detect guilt in a suspect – in other words he was using the twig as a divining tool, just like the modern diviner's pendulum. After visiting the wine merchant's house to get the scent like a bloodhound, Aymar's rod led him on a long and complicated journey to the prison in the small town of Beaucaire in the Camargue, more than 200 kilometres from Lyons. Inside the jail, Aymar's rod identified as the guilty party a hunchback who had just been arrested for petty larceny. At first the hunchback denied all knowledge of the crime. But when he was taken back to Lyons along the route that Aymar had traced, the hunchback is said to have confessed that though he had not murdered the vintner and his wife himself – a couple of other men had done that – he had helped them carry away their spoils. In the end, the two alleged murderers could not be traced. But the hunchback was condemned to death and broken on the wheel before a huge crowd in Lyons.[7], [8]

Such use of the rod to apportion guilt alarmed churchmen who appealed to Malebranche for guidance. The philosopher said that he knew the rod was used to find mineral veins and water and this could be explained by the influence on the rod of subtle, invisible bodies (corpuscles) emitted by them. But Malebranche had never heard of the use of the forked twig to resolve moral issues. If, as in the case of Aymar, the rod seemed indeed capable of correctly identifying criminals, then, reasoned Malebranche, there must be a supernatural cause. But because God could not be expected to concern Himself with such petty matters, the cause must therefore be sought in the work of infernal spirits.[9]

That a philosopher like Malebranche could be driven to arguments of this kind illustrates the intellectual chaos that can ensue when dowsing is confused with divination. What is significant is that Gassendi, Malebranche and other thinkers of the time recognized dowsing as a natural phenomenon that could be explained in terms of current scientific theory and had nothing to do with the supernatural.

Probably because of the fame of its exponents, the idea that atoms or corpuscles rose from the vein and interacted with corresponding particles in the rod, thereby causing it to move, emerged as the most popular theory of dowsing in the seventeenth and eighteenth centuries. But there were several alternative ideas. Some early dowsing theorists, probably influenced by classical writers such as the Roman architect Vitruvius Pollio and the Roman natural historian Pliny the Elder, held that warm, dry metallic vapours from the vein, rather than atoms or corpuscles, caused the rod to move. Others supported the rather mystical notion that the various metals in the Earth attracted the different woods or metals from which the dowser's rod was made.

This concept of 'sympathetic attraction' seems to have been around from the very start of dowsing – Agricola recorded that some miners used hazel rods to locate silver, ash rods for copper, pitch pine ones for lead and tin, while iron rods were used for gold. Robert Fludd (1574–1637), the English mystical philosopher and Rosicrucian, was a prominent advocate of this idea.[10] Fludd regarded dowsing as a manifestation of the 'occult' property of the hazel tree to respond to minerals hidden deep in the Earth. In the eyes of Fludd, the hazel's attraction to concealed metals seemed no more surprising than that of the lodestone to iron or the Earth's north magnetic pole.

Whatever their fame, none of these philosophers seem to have carefully observed dowsers at work. Had they done so, they would have noted, as Agricola did, that not everyone can dowse – the rod twists only in the hands of certain people. This simple observation rules out a direct interaction between any unseen influence from the vein and the rod.

The first man to try to prove this point experimentally was Athanasius Kircher (1602–1680), the German-born Jesuit experimental scientist and thinker. Kircher had a 'see for yourself' attitude to science. Curious to find out more about the

Earth's interior, he had himself lowered into the crater of Vesuvius to get a close look at the strata.

Kircher adopted the same approach to dowsing. He balanced dowsing rods of various woods next to metals in such a way that if the metal really attracted the wood, the rods would dip. They did not. Kircher concluded that the dowser was duped by the power of his own imagination into thinking that his rod dipped of its own accord when in fact he himself was inadvertently twisting it.[11, 12]

Of course, Kircher's attempt to model the dowsing situation was naïve by present-day standards. Small pieces of metal in a laboratory are very different from veins of metal ore deposited in faults or fracture zones. Strictly speaking, his experiments leave open the possibility that some influence associated with ore veins in the field, but not pieces of metal in a laboratory, does indeed attract the dowser's rod. But if Kircher's experiments were imperfect, at least he deserves credit for performing them – and few today would quarrel with his conclusions. Since Kircher's time, almost all serious students of dowsing – believers and sceptics alike – have agreed that the explanation of dowsing lies in the behaviour of the dowser rather than that of the rod.

Athanasius Kircher was not the only seventeenth-century scientist who devoted time to dowsing experiments. Robert Boyle, whose interest in Somerset mineral dowsing we have already noted, carried out some experiments of his own, but found that in his own hands the rod did not seem to respond to metals or metallic veins. Essentially, therefore, he confirmed the observations of Agricola and Kircher: the rod does not move for everyone, so the dowser himself must twist it. But, Boyle acknowledged that, even so, some people might still be able to detect mineral veins successfully with the rod, concluding: 'But of the Experiment I must content myself to say what I am wont to do when my opinion is ask'd of those things I dare not peremptorily reject and yet am not convinced of, namely that they have seen them can much more reasonably believe them than they that have not'.[13]

Some thirty years after Boyle had published his work on dowsing, another French savant, Pierre Le Lorrain, Abbé de Vallemont, wrote a treatise on the subject, published in 1693.[14] At this time the publicity given to Aymar's exploits had made dowsing a topic of great interest to fashionable Paris society and the corpuscular theory, as outlined by Gassendi, Malebranche and others, was much in vogue.

Having a closer knowledge of dowsing than his more distinguished fellow countrymen, de Vallemont could see the limitations of the corpuscular theory, and tried to improve it. Recognizing that dowsing ability varied from one person to another, he concluded that the dowser himself played at least as an important part in dowsing as his rod. Perhaps, de Vallemont suggested, the dowsing faculty varied like other human senses such as sight and hearing, the rod serving merely to magnify the body's natural dowsing sensitivity to corpuscles from the vein, just as a telescope lets someone see things that would otherwise remain invisible.

So by the start of the eighteenth century, a wide choice of theories were available to explain the apparent response of the dowser or his rod to the concealed mineral vein. Moreover some of these theories had the backing of some of the leading thinkers of the time. The fact that scientists and philosophers like Gassendi, Malebranche and Boyle had taken dowsing seriously was crucial in winning respect and status for European mine dowsers in the early eighteenth century.

Throughout this heyday of dowsing, the technique nevertheless had its critics. Some believed dowsing to be nothing but a fraud. For instance in his *Miners' Dictionary* William Hooson, a Derbyshire mining expert, related the story that the technique was the invention of a German who was 'deservedly hanged as a cheat'.[15]

Despite the fact that some clergymen, like the Abbé de Vallemont, were supporters of dowsing, there were many within the Church who opposed it. These critics now argued in a very cunning way. They attacked dowsing first because it didn't work and second because it did.

Several clergymen amassed evidence to show that dowsing did not really work. Jacques Aymar was brought to Paris and failed in several tests to see if his rod moved over buried metals.[16] The investigators then devised a more appropriate test for the Dauphiné peasant. A few days before, a swordsman had stabbed a sentry to death in the Rue Saint Denis. Yet, when Aymar was asked to find the spot where the man had been killed, his rod did not move in the right place. The clergy were not impressed with Aymar's excuses, one of which was that his rod would not turn if the swordsman had been drunk when he committed the crime.

Other clergy argued somewhat as Malebranche had done, but went further. They acknowledged dowsers' achievements, but claimed that all successful use of the rod – not just divination of guilt in a suspect – could only be the work of the Devil or his minions. Indeed, several books appeared in the early eighteenth century depicting clergymen unmasking a dowser to reveal his horns, tail and cloven hooves.

The irrefutable logic of these clerical arguments clearly impressed the Holy See for in 1702 the Vatican placed de Vallemont's treatise on its list of prohibited books.

Despite scientific scepticism and the Vatican's attitude, mineral dowsing continued to flourish, reaching, as we have seen, a peak of development in the middle years of the eighteenth century. Yet, from that time onward, dowsing for metal ores entered a long period of decline. By the mid-nineteenth century, when new mines were opening up all over the world to provide the metals needed by the Industrial Revolution, most miners had come to regard dowsing as a quaint superstition rather than an effective prospecting technique.

What were the reasons for this change in attitude? It seems unlikely that the clergy's views concerning the rôle of the Devil in dowsing carried much weight in mining circles. Despite the publicity given to Aymar's failures to find buried metals under test, it is also unlikely that experimental evidence played much part.

The real cause, surely, was that as science progressed during the eighteenth and early nineteenth centuries, the best-known theories of dowsing – the corpuscular theory and the idea of sympathetic attraction – came to look hopelessly out of date. Although more promising theories were becoming available – for example de Vallemont's emphasis of the rôle of the dowser rather than the rod, and a later attempt, by the French physician Pierre Thouvenel, to explain dowsing in the electrical terms then fashionable[17, 18] – they evidently attracted little notice. With no theoretical support, the professional mine dowsers could no longer defend themselves from the attacks of sceptics and clergy and in the end their craft just withered away.

For more than a century, the ancient art of locating mineral veins with a forked twig seems to have been almost extinct. In Cornwall, the German mining regions and elsewhere some miners may have passed the technique on from father to son. From time to time, no doubt, an older miner may have demonstrated his prowess at tracing the course of a lode. But generally mining experts appear to have viewed the practice with more amusement than amazement. Then, in the late 1960s, the old technique was suddenly resurrected in what might seem to be the most unexpected of places: Russia and the other republics of the former Soviet Union.

When we recall that the chief reason for the decline of European mine dowsing in the eighteenth century was the lack of supporting theory, the technique's resuscitation in what was then the Soviet Union does not seem so surprising. For in the

1960s immense exploration programmes for minerals of all kinds were under way there. Many new prospecting techniques, such as geochemical and geobotanical methods, were being assessed. The scale of the exploration activity demanded the use of all possible methods and in this context it seemed quite natural to look again at the ancient art of dowsing – even if no one quite knew how it worked.

If a group of Western scientists were proposing to use dowsing in geological exploration, their first act would be to assemble a team of investigators from appropriate disciplines – physics, biology, geology, psychology and so on. The team would then be briefed first to confirm that a dowsing effect really existed and, second, if it did, to uncover its mechanism. Only then would it be possible to start using the technique in the field. The Russian dowser-geologists appear to have tried very hard to get the authorities to carry out such a study. But their arguments did not carry the day and no such work was undertaken. All that seems to have happened was that a few inconclusive experiments were carried out under the auspices of the All-Union Institute of Mining.

Undaunted, however, the Russian dowser-geologists did what would not in these circumstances have been possible in the West. Leaving theory aside as a problem for the future, they went ahead and developed their own special dowsing methods. The first thing the geologists did was to try and quantify the technique. To do this they devised special dowsing rods that could rotate completely in the hands as the dowser walked along.

In fact, it is quite easy to make a Russian dowser's rod from ordinary coat-hanger wire. First, straighten out the wire until you have a length of about 1 metre. Then twist the wire right round to make a small loop right in the middle. Now you can make one side of the rod by making two right-angle bends in the wire. Make the first by bending the wire towards you about 10 centimetres from the loop. Make the second bend, about 15 centimetres further on, by bending the wire in the other direction so that the end of the rod is parallel to the centre part with the loop. Then form the other half of the rod in the same way. You should end up with a rod looking like the profile of a broad-brimmed hat.

Using this rod can be quite a strange experience. For sometimes it really does twist right round in your hands as you walk along. To dowse like a Soviet geologist, all you need to do is to record the number of times the rod turns round as you walk over a certain distance. The geologists actually designed an automatic revolution counter to record this.

Before looking at the way the Soviet geologists used their dowsing rods in their search for the hidden mineral wealth of their vast country, it is worth comparing the challenges they faced with those encountered by the miners of eighteenth century Europe. In Cornwall and Germany, dowsers typically used their rods to trace the exact positions of mineral lodes in existing mining areas. In the former Soviet Union, on the other hand, the need was for dowsers to help in mineral exploration on a vast scale. While metal-bearing lodes of the Cornish or German type are found in Russia and some of the other republics, there are also many other kinds of mineral deposit: immense masses of copper and zinc sulphides and chromium ore, diamond pipes, deposits of rare earth metals – used to make TV screens – and so on. To get a better idea of where rich metal ores were likely to be found in little-explored regions, the Soviet geologists also needed to know the positions of geological faults – great cracks where past earthquakes have caused the rocks of the Earth's crust to fracture.

To see how useful dowsing might be in the search for mineral wealth, Valery Matveev, one of the geologist-dowsers, carried out tests in 1967 near the Tasti-Butak copper deposits in Kazakhstan. He claimed that when dowsers walked over concealed copper-zinc sulphide ore bodies, their rods rotated rapidly – at least one revolution for each metre covered. When different dowsers walked along the same path, their rods tended to rotate in the same places.

Following the publication in a reputable scientific journal of Matveev's first experiments,[19] other Soviet geologists realized that they need no longer conceal their dowsing proclivities. All over the republics of the former Soviet Union, from the frozen wastes of Yakutia to the deserts of Kazakhstan and the high mountain homelands of the Tadzik and Kirghiz peoples, the geologists marched with their rotating rods.[20] They said that their devices revolved most often over mineral veins, sulphide or chromite ore bodies, diamond pipes and certain gold deposits.

The geologists claimed that dowsing had helped them find deposits of rare earth elements in Karelia, metal sulphide deposits in Kazakhstan and tin-tungsten veins in Kirghizstan and Tadzikstan. Apart from mineral veins and ore bodies, the geologists had found dowsing particularly useful in locating concealed faults and fracture zones. For instance, the Moscow geologist Mikhail Komin reported that dowsing had proved helpful in determining the general direction of faults and fractures in a region he had been mapping. The dowsing results were later confirmed by magnetic surveying. Tatia Burova, another Moscow geologist, had successfully used dowsing to help pinpoint the location of rare earth, tin and tungsten ore bodies in Kirghizstan and Tadzikstan. She had also used the technique to find the direction of the fractures that had played a part in controlling the location of the tin deposits.

Valery Matveev and Nikolai Sochevanov, another Moscow geologist, reported that, while making a dowsing survey in northern Kazakhstan, four dowsers had independently located two particular dowsing zones. Boreholes were drilled to see what, if anything, they had discovered. Beneath the first dowsing zone the drillers found a fault, with a little iron sulphide. A substantial copper-zinc sulphide ore body was discovered beneath the second.[21]

On another occasion, in north Karelia, the geologists carried out a dowsing survey by helicopter. The dowser sat in the aircraft, holding a rod the dip of which was recorded automatically as the helicopter's crew carried out a photographic survey of the area. When plotted afterwards, the dip of the rod showed a good correlation with the positions of local fracture zones, where rare metal deposits were subsequently found by drilling.

Impressed by the activities of their Soviet colleagues, geologists in some other Eastern bloc countries also started to use dowsing in the field. In one instance,[22] Dr Slobodan Stoici, Chief Geologist of a copper mine in the Bihor Mountains of western Romania, and entirely sceptical about dowsing, agreed to participate in a dowsing demonstration. The study took place in an area in the mountains nearby, which had been mined for copper and lead in the seventeenth and eighteenth centuries.

The area was forested, with deep soil cover which prevented any clues to mineralization in the underlying metamorphic rocks being visible at the surface. Two dowsers, Andrei Apostol and Dan Svoronos, first carried out a systematic dowsing survey of the area, obtaining a pattern of responses which they attributed to several faults, two of which seemed to intersect at a point in the forest. After the dowsing work, the geologists carried out geochemical and geophysical surveys in the same area. Both of these suggested anomalies – probably due to a hidden sulphide ore body – around precisely the same point. As a result of this confirmation of dowsing results by subsequent surveys, Dr Stoici became convinced of the value of the ancient art.

Despite all the Eastern bloc geologists' work, however, which involved the contributions of hundreds of individuals, the organization of two major conferences and the drilling of thousands of boreholes, in scientific terms their attempt to revive the ancient art of mineral dowsing must be counted a failure. Not only did they fail to stimulate any Western scientific interest in dowsing, they even failed to convince the majority of their own colleagues that dowsing was an effective prospecting technique.

The first failure is easy to explain. Leaving language barriers aside, for many years Western scientists had, even in orthodox fields of enquiry, questioned the experimental standards of many of their Eastern bloc counterparts. When these pariahs broached the already disreputable subject of dowsing, there was little chance that Western scientists would take them seriously.

As to the geologists' failure to convince their own colleagues, several factors may have played a part. One was the failure to carry out properly controlled experiments. Another was the propensity of some Soviet dowsers to confuse dowsing with divination and make wildly extravagant claims. Some claimed almost unbelievable accuracy in locating drilling sites – far better than could be obtained by geophysical methods. Others said they could divine the precise depth, dimensions and metal content of ore bodies. Yet others claimed that they could, as if twiddling the knobs of a radio, 'tune in' to particular underground metals, instructing their rods to respond only to gold, copper and so on. Orthodox Soviet geologists seized on these unrealistic claims as evidence that dowsing was just an outmoded superstition.[23]

But perhaps the most important weakness, in the eyes of their colleagues, was the geologists' inability to provide any convincing theory of dowsing. The factor that had led to the decline of European mine dowsing in the eighteenth century operated again in the Soviet Union two centuries later.

How much, then, did the Soviet geologists achieve when they resurrected the ancient art of mineral dowsing with such enthusiasm? Certainly, for the reasons outlined above, we cannot accept their work as a rigorous validation of dowsing by modern science. They did, however, confirm on a large scale what William Cookworthy had noted in 1778: some dowsers not only have an uncanny ability to find mineral veins and lodes, they seem equally capable of finding unmineralized faults and fracture zones. Good dowsers seem to respond to cracks and fissures in the Earth's crust, whether or not they contain the metal ores so prized by industrial society.

So could there be some truth in the old dowsing theories after all? While today we may laugh at the notion of corpuscles rising from the hidden vein and dragging the rod down, could other subtle influences, linked with these huge cracks in the Earth cause dowsers to twist their rods? Could this explain other facets of the dowsers' art, as well as the search for minerals?

2 The Water Finders

In the 1920s W.W. Varvill, a mining engineer, was prospecting for lead ore veins near Pateley Bridge in Yorkshire, England.[1] One of the local miners claimed that he could find mineral veins with his forked hazel twig. So Varvill and his foreman – both sceptical about dowsing – devised a test for the miner. They blindfolded him and then guided him along a path over the nearby Greenhow Hill which they suspected would pass over a group of mineral veins. There were no visible signs of mineralization and the limestone beneath was covered with peat and heather.

As the three of them approached the place where Varvill suspected the presence of mineral veins, the dowser said, 'Ah'm comin' to summat.' Then, a little later, his hazel rod twisted up so violently that the point hit his chest. When they returned along the same path, the miner's rod moved in exactly the same place. Later on, Varvill studied a local geological map and found that a well-known geological fracture – the North Craven Fault – crossed the path near the place where the dowser's rod had hit his chest. At this point the fault, which was visible in the Bradford Corporation Aqueduct Tunnel running beneath the hill, consisted of a band of shattered rock several metres wide, separating shales on the north from limestone to the south. Varvill pointed out that such a fault zone would form an important underground water channel.

This anecdote helps us solve a riddle that has baffled people for centuries – why dowsers seemingly respond to substances as different as metal ores and water. In Varvill's account, a dowser seeking mineral veins ended up finding a water-bearing fracture zone. On reflection, this is precisely what we might expect. Because water often fills the same fractures or fissures as minerals, and if – as the evidence in the last chapter suggests – dowsers really can detect these fractures, they will also appear to detect any water flowing within them.

In fact, miners have always been aware of the link between minerals and water. When driving a tunnel ahead below the water table, water may sometimes rush into a mine, often at such a rate that extra pumping equipment has to be brought in. When this happens, the source of the water is usually a fault or fracture zone that has just been penetrated by the tunnel. Indeed, one of the tasks of mine geologists today is to map the local geological structure so that the positions of water-bearing fissures can be predicted.

Bearing this in mind, it seems likely that seventeenth-century mine dowsers sought 'water veins' for precisely the same reasons as miners do today: to predict where water would most likely enter the mine. But if the miners were interested in water for negative reasons, others required it for its own sake. Peasants living in mining areas, learning that dowsers could find water as well as minerals, probably started to dowse for much-needed water themselves. It is likely that this was how water dowsing first developed as an art in its own right.

The first water dowser to achieve fame, however, was neither a miner nor a peasant, but a Frenchwoman of gentle birth, Martine de Bertereau. Born in the province of Touraine towards the end of the sixteenth century, she married a nobleman from Brabant, Jean de Châstelet, Baron de Beausoleil et d'Auffenbach. The Baron became perhaps the world's leading mining expert, and it was through his work that his wife acquired her almost obsessional interest in mineralogical matters and dowsing.

The Baron de Beausoleil's combination of high rank and technical expertise gained him many commissions as mining adviser to the princes of Europe. Under the Holy Roman Emperors Rudolph II and Matthias he held the appointment of Commissioner General of the three Chambers of Mines of Hungary. He also worked both for the Austrian Archduke Leopold as director of mines in the Tyrol and Trent and as mining adviser to successive Dukes of Bavaria. At one time, the Baron even served as mining adviser to the Pope, his brief covering all the Apostolic estates.

These mining posts gave the Baron and his wife unrivalled opportunities for studying the mines of Europe. Martine de Beausoleil took full advantage of these chances. Not content with learning about prospecting and how to recognize the various minerals, she descended deep into the subterranean shafts and tunnels and tunnels of great mines such as Chemnitz in Germany and Bibertallen in Hungary. It seems that she had even travelled as far as Peru, where she had crawled through the underground passages of the fabulously wealthy silver mines of Potosi.

To complement her practical knowledge of mining and mineralogy, the Baroness studied ancient texts such as Pliny the Elder's *Natural History* together with the few more recent technical studies of mining that were then available.

The Baroness seems to have learnt about water dowsing from miners in the Italian-speaking Alpine regions of Trent and the Tyrol – where her husband was at one time Director of Mines. Having observed how the miners dowsed for water, she then did the same thing herself. In 1629, together with one of her sons, she stayed for several weeks in the small town of Château-Thierry, some eighty kilometres north-east of Paris. According to her own account, before entering the town she used her 'instruments' – at this stage she did not mention dowsing rods by name – to find out if there were any mineral deposits there. She boasted, 'I found several sources of mineral water. I summoned Officers of Justice, Doctors and Apothecaries of the town to see the proof of my discovery and attest to the quality of the water.'[2]

Martine de Beausoleil explained that in her view the underground water had passed through minerals containing silver and gold, iron and vitriol (sulphate minerals) in abundance. As a result, the water should be effective in the treatment of liver conditions, removing kidney stones, arresting dysentery and in dealing with various other medical conditions.

The Baroness's discovery of the Château-Thierry mineral springs[3] was only one of many finds that the Beausoleils made in France. In 1626 the Baron obtained a commission under the Marquis d'Effiat, superintendent of mines in France, to advise the State concerning mining ventures. The couple brought with them to France a large team of mine workers from Germany and Hungary and carried out what seems to have been one of the world's first properly organized mineral reconnaissance programmes: a seventeenth-century forerunner of the US Geological Survey. In her report on the work the Baroness listed existing mines and known mineral deposits; for instance lead, silver and tin deposits in Brittany, amethyst mines in the Auvergne, yellow amber finds in Picardy and lead and silver deposits in Provence.[4] The team seem to have discovered some of these deposits themselves, and it is almost certain that they used dowsing – albeit surreptitiously.

Martine de Beausoleil and her husband appear to have devoted their whole lives to science – though the Baroness also found time to bring up at least four children. Such dedication is not always understood today and in the superstition-filled climate of the seventeenth century it must have seemed so incomprehensible as to arouse the deepest suspicions. Together with her rumoured use of the rod – which, because of its links with magic and divination, had been condemned as the work of the Devil by some churchmen as early as 1518 – and the many foreign connections of the Baron, it was enough to make the couple many enemies in France.

The first hint of the approaching storm came in 1627, when the couple were prospecting in the Buisson-Rochemares Forest in Brittany. A provost of the Duke of Brittany called Le Touche-Grippé surprised them there and, under the pretext that they were practising magic, took away all their instruments, mineral specimens, reports, maps of mines together with much money. While the Baron was later able to defend himself against the charges brought against him in the French courts, the Beausoleils' demands for the punishment of Le Touche-Grippé and the return of their property were refused. The couple returned to Germany in despair.

But the real danger to the de Beausoleils did not come until the 1640s, after the Baroness had published a book called *La Restitution de Pluton*.[5] This she dedicated to Cardinal Richelieu, then the real power behind the French throne. In this flattering work, the Baroness argued that if the Cardinal would develop the hidden mineral wealth of the country, France would become the most fortunate of nations. In her own verse:

> France and the French ask you for mines,
> Gold, silver, azure, lodestone, calamines,
> They are treasures hidden by the spirit of God,
> If you authorise what I propose,
> You will see, Monseigneur, without metamorphose,
> France will truly become a 'Riche-lieu'

Tragically, neither the couple's herculean labours, nor the Baroness's patriotic sentiments were enough to offset the effects of a fateful slip that she had made in this document. While previously reticent about her prospecting methods, in this document she was explicit. Anyone looking for mineral veins should first, she said, look for excavations in the Earth – where the metal ores may themselves be seen. Then the prospector should closely examine the local vegetation – this might give important clues. Next, she said, pay attention to the taste of water and the 'vapours which arise from mountains and valleys at dawn'.

Then came the passage that was to lead to her downfall. The Baroness wrote, 'There are seven dowsing rods of which the knowledge and practice is most necessary, which the ancients used to discover from the surface metals hidden in the depths. And also to discover sources of water.'

Martine de Beausoleil's endorsement of dowsing seems to have been just the admission the couple's enemies were seeking. Cardinal Richelieu had the Baron and Baroness arrested and incarcerated in separate prisons – he in the Bastille and she in the Château de Vincennes.[6, 7] Not even their children escaped this terrible fate. One of the daughters – whom the Baroness was teaching mineralogy – was locked up with her mother, while one of her sons, when visiting the Baron in the Bastille, was also locked away. Separated both from each other and the mines to which they were so devoted, the two pioneering mineralogists died behind bars.

But the tragic death of the first famous water dowser did not halt the growth of this branch of the art. As the Baroness had herself reported, by the early seventeenth century miners in the southern Alps were already using their rods to search for underground water as well as mineral veins. By the end of the century, the Alpine miners appear to have transmitted the art of water dowsing to peasants in the neighbouring Dauphiné region of south-eastern France – Jacques Aymar came from these parts. In England, by a similar process, water dowsing seems to have diffused outward from the lead and zinc mines of the Mendip Hills to the surrounding countryside. Here it became so entrenched that some of the world's best-known dowsers would later come from this region of England.

The full story of how the art of searching for underground water with a forked twig spread outward from the mining regions to the surrounding country areas has yet to be told. But, by the end of the eighteenth century, dowsers in many parts of Europe were practising this form of the art. Presumably the extent to which it flourished depended on the local needs for water – dowsing would have been favoured in dry areas or regions such as limestone terrane where water was difficult to find.

As Europeans colonized the world in the eighteenth and nineteenth centuries, they took water dowsing with them. The Russians conquered northern Asia, the French established themselves in parts of North America and Africa and the British founded colonies in every continent. As the Spanish conquistadores had already introduced mineral dowsing into South America, by the end of the nineteenth century the use of the forked twig had spread to almost every corner of the globe.

At first sight it seems odd that water dowsers should thrive just at the time when mineral dowsing was dying out. But on reflection, the reason becomes clear. Mineral dowsing was a professional activity, practised by mining experts and underpinned by the views of some of the leading thinkers of the time. When the theories supporting mineral dowsing collapsed, the professional mining men abandoned it, just as mining corporations today discard outmoded techniques.

Water dowsing, by contrast, was largely a pastime of amateurs. The technique passed on from father to son in rural tradition was not affected by developments in scientific thought. The country water dowsers neither knew nor cared that men of science now viewed their craft as a quaint superstition. What mattered for them and the farming communities they served was not the latest scientific theory but that the technique seemed to work.

So, as scientific understanding grew of how water flows in the ground, the claims of the rural water dowsers seemed more and more archaic. The scientists developed mathematical descriptions of how water from rain and snow sinks into the ground and slowly flows through the pores of sedimentary rocks such as sandstones. The dowsers, however, continued to search for 'water veins', just as the seventeenth-century miners had done. Even in regions underlain by permeable sediments, the dowsers continued to believe that all underground water flowed in veins. To this day, most water dowsers still cling to this antiquated notion.

Therefore, in addition to difficulties presented by the lack of supporting theory, the water dowsers' archaic ideas about the flow of underground water created a further obstacle to the scientific acceptance of their art. No wonder many geologists came to view the technique with suspicion.

However, in ridiculing those dowsers who find water veins everywhere, geologists sometimes fail to acknowledge that the dowsers' old-fashioned ideas really do make sense in some situations. For instance, in the areas of crystalline rock where many mines are sited, water does indeed flow in fissures and fractures just as the early miners noticed. In limestone regions, too, water is often confined to underground cavities that have been created by the dissolving action of the water itself. Again, in regions made up of old volcanic lavas and ashes, the water often flows in fissures or cracks between the lava blocks or even in the long cavernous lava tubes that run the length of many old lava flows. In such areas, geologists often have the greatest difficulty in siting wells that will yield enough water. It is in precisely these districts, where underground water flows in cracks and fissures, that many dowsers have flourished and a few have produced quite outstanding results.

One of the first such dowsers to win fame was a French herdsman, Barthelemy Bléton.[8, 9] Born in the same Dauphiné region that had produced Jacques Aymar, Bléton's unusual abilities are said to have manifested themselves when he was only seven. According to the story, while taking lunch to some workmen, the lad sat down on a stone to rest, but was then seized with a fever. The workmen called him away from the stone and the fever left him. But whenever the boy returned to the stone, he suffered again. Later, the ground beneath the stone was dug up revealing a spring of water which was later used to run a mill.

Whether or not you believe the story of how Bléton's alleged sensitivity to underground water was discovered, some of his later achievements certainly seem impressive. The young herdsman used an unusual dowsing tool: instead of the forked twig he balanced a slightly curved wand on the tops of his two outstretched forefingers. When he experienced a dowsing response, his fingers caused the rod to rotate up to eighty times per minute. Bléton's rod was in a way a forerunner of the revolving devices later used by Soviet geologists.

Bléton's success in finding a source of mineral waters at Contrexéville, near the Vosges Mountains attracted the attention of Dr Pierre Thouvenel, Inspector General of Mineral Waters of France. Thouvenel took Bléton to Paris where, like Jacques Aymar a century before, the dowser was put through a series of tests.

In one, Bléton was blindfolded and tested to see if he could trace the course of an underground aqueduct that ran under the Luxembourg Gardens in Paris. According to the *Journal de Paris*, 13 May 1782, the Dauphiné herdsman managed to trace the twists and turns of the aqueduct with great precision. The experiment was repeated with Bléton blindfolded in front of a crowd of five hundred distinguished onlookers, including ministers, ambassadors, clergymen and scientists. The *Journal de Paris* reported 'Bléton has followed more than fifteen thousand bends of the conduits without his having committed a single error.'

Bléton's impressive dowsing performances attracted the attention of the highest in the land. The Queen of France, the ill-fated Marie Antoinette, employed him to site wells at the Palace of Versailles. Although, according to some reports, Bléton was entirely successful in finding water for the Queen, according to others he did have some failures, mistaking caverns and dry conduits for those containing water.

Such so-called failures have important implications for dowsing theory. Remember that, according to William Pryce, dowsers cannot distinguish between poor lodes and rich ones and that the dowser in Varvill's anecdote could not tell the difference between a mineral vein and a water-filled fracture zone. Bléton's inability to distinguish between dry underground conduits and those filled with water corroborates these observations. Dowsers may, it seems, detect underground features, but they cannot tell what they are.

Of course, case histories such as the story of Bléton's

achievements in Paris and Versailles are by themselves of limited scientific value. But, taken together with his other successes in water-finding and tracing features beneath the ground, they surely suggest that his claims were worth investigating thoroughly. The kind of investigator needed was an open-minded scientist who would carefully examine Bléton's results to see if the herdsman could have obtained his information by conventional means.

Unfortunately, as has so often happened in dowsing, the scientist who chose to assess Bléton's claims, the astronomer Joseph-Jérôme de Lalande (1732–1807), had preconceived ideas on the subject. Ignoring the serious issue – whether Bléton really could detect underground features – Lalande denounced the dowser as a charlatan and his mentor, Thouvenel, as a fraud solely because the dowser himself caused his wand to rotate, by moving his fingers.[10] The famous astronomer was clearly far too busy to look closely into the evidence and obliviously unaware that the rôle of the dowser in moving the rod had already been recognized for centuries. Like several later outspoken sceptics, Lalande used the prestige of his position to dismiss dowsing on a priori grounds.

Lalande's dismissal of dowsing purely on the grounds that the rod does not move of its own accord set a pattern which later French intellectuals followed. The most influential of these was the long-lived chemist and pioneering psychologist Michel-Eugène Chevreul (1786–1889), whose view that dowsing is nothing more than self-deception[11] has been accepted without question by generations of French scientists.[12] So, although many dowsers flourished in France during the nineteenth and twentieth centuries, their claims were largely ignored by geologists and other scientists. As a result, little further solid evidence concerning dowsing achievements accumulated in France.

To continue this strange story of the water finders, we need to cross the English Channel. For in Britain, with its empirical rather than rational tradition, nineteenth-century scientists were more willing than their French counterparts to look at dowsing in an unprejudiced manner. No less a figure than Sir Archibald Geikie (1835–1924), the energetic Scottish geologist who became Director-General of the British Geological Survey, made a careful study of the subject and concluded that the evidence in favour of dowsing was so striking that he was keeping his mind open on the question. Several other distinguished British and Irish geologists of the Victorian period were equally impressed by the dowsing evidence.

Who, then, were the characters whose seeming ability to find underground water convinced these hard-headed scientists? One of the first was the Bristol-born stone-mason and father of twenty-six children, William Scott Lawrence, who dowsed successfully for nearly seventy years until his death in 1896.[13] Lawrence's excellent record in locating wells in the West Country of England won him testimonials from many titled landowners as well as the Bristol Wagon Works, the Tiverton Town Council, and the Great Western Railway.

Another West Country water finder of high repute was the Wiltshire farmer, Benjamin Tompkins. To give an example of one of his successes, in 1893 water was urgently required at Toy Farm, in a chalk valley near Newhaven in Sussex. A well 51 metres deep had been dug but no water was found. So Benjamin Tompkins was called in. He chose a site about 140 metres further up the valley than the first well. After digging through chalk with flints for 36 metres, water suddenly rushed into the new well. In reporting on the case afterwards, the geologist Ernest Westlake concluded that Tompkins' success was due to the fact that he had sited the well right on top of a fissure in the chalk.

Yet another successful West Country dowser of the period was the Wiltshire-born well-sinker, William Stone. According to Sir William Barrett, Stone was 'a shrewd business man not marred by any undue sense of modesty and with a very inflated notion of his own importance'. Although these personal characteristics make some of his own claims difficult to evaluate, there is no doubt that Stone acquired a solid record of success in water finding. For instance, on one occasion, Stone was called in to find water on an estate near Newry in northern Ireland. The underlying rock was granite, where water could only be found in fissures, and the owner of the estate had sunk at least one well without finding water. Stone chose a site where he said there would be a good supply. After quarrying through the granite for six metres, a splendid spring was found. Stone had evidently located the well on a deep fissure, for it yielded a large and constant supply of water, even during the spring and summer, when other local springs were dry.

But of all the British dowsers of Victorian times, the one with the highest reputation of all was John Mullins, the son of a Wiltshire stone-mason. Unlike Stone, Mullins was a modest, down-to-earth man, with, in the words of one of his clients 'the honest look of a John Bull master mason'.

In one instance, recorded by Sir J.J. Thomson, the eminent British physicist,[14] Mullins found water for a farm belonging to Trinity College, Cambridge. Thomson, a Fellow of Trinity, wrote:

The water supply to one of our farms was very defective and a new well badly wanted. At first the Senior Bursar, who was a Fellow of the Royal Society, proceeded in the orthodox way and employed eminent geologists to report on where we ought to sink a well. Their advice, however, did not lead to the discovery of any water. Our land agent said 'If I were you, I would try old X [Mullins], who has found a good many wells in this county and who will sink the well on the terms 'no water, no pay'. As there seemed nothing else to be done, the Bursar employed him and he found water.

In another case, in 1879, a railway company required a large supply of water for their locomotives. The well needed to be close to the rails at Shepton Mallet Station in Somerset. The contractor to the railway company had sunk a well 76 metres deep through the local shales without finding a drop of water. After much hesitation, the contractor asked Mullins to help out. With his forked twig, Mullins selected a site, about 15 metres away from the old well, where he said an abundance of water would be found. Mullins advised the contractor to drive a heading from the well to a point beneath the place where his twig had turned. When this was done, such a flood of water poured into the well that the workmen had to rush for their lives, abandoning their drills, hammers and clothes.[15]

On another occasion, a certain H.W. Hoskyns required a pure supply of water on his estate near Crewkerne in Somerset. The only existing source of water was an old well that was so polluted that it could not be used. Mullins was brought in and his hazel rod twisted over a site about 15 metres away from the old well. A new well was sunk on this site. When the diggers reached a depth of about 8 metres, they hit a joint or fissure in the limestone. Water rushed into the well rapidly, its level rising to within one metre of the surface. The new well yielded a constant supply of pure water, quite unrelated to the polluted source in the old well nearby.

At the request of the physicist Sir William Barrett, the geologist Ernest Westlake looked into this case. He concluded that Mullins had located his well over a fault which brought a well-known local clay formation, the Fullers Earth, against the limestone. The clay was damming the water up in the limestone, hence the high yield of the well.

One of Mullins' most celebrated water-finding achievements was for a firm of bacon curers in Waterford, Ireland. In 1887, the company, Messrs Richardsons, needed a large supply of water at their premises just south of the River Suir, to the west of Waterford. The rocks beneath were ancient slates and grits locally covered with clays and gravels left behind by glaciers during the most recent ice age.

The firm first had a hole bored for 89 metres but without finding water. A year later, the company had another hole, 290 metres deep, bored some 60 metres away from the first hole. This too was a failure. So the firm then asked G.H. Kinahan, the senior geologist of the Irish Geological Survey, to select a site. He did so, choosing a point about 90 metres away from the first hole. This hole was bored to a depth of about 15 metres, but yielded only 17 litres per minute – less than a tenth of what was required.

So, in desperation, the bacon curers sent for Mullins. Soon after arriving on the boat from England, the dowser was seen walking around with his hazel twig. At a point about 60 metres from the first well the rod suddenly twisted so violently in Mullins' hands that it broke. The dowser said that water would be found anywhere along a line going north-east through this point.

The company had a further hole bored at the spot where Mullins' rod had twisted. After drilling through about 12 metres of the glacial clays and gravels and then 12 metres of grit, they encountered slate. At this point the drillers took a sounding and found 11 metres of water in the tube. The supply of water exceeded the capacity of the pump – about 130 litres per minute – and its quality and temperature were ideal for the bacon curers' purposes.

When Kinahan heard of Mullins' success, he was unstinting with his praise. The geologist wrote that Mullins must have found the water by instinct 'due either to his being able to smell water or that water has such an influence on his nervous system that he can tell the distance and quantity when he is near it; unless he was a Sherlock Holmes who could draw conclusions from trifles that no one else could detect' and 'As far as actual results went I failed, and the diviner "wiped my eye".'[16]

But what was the actual reason for Mullins' success at Waterford? Another geologist with the Irish Geological Survey, J.R. Kilroe, shed light on this in an official report which he made on the borings. Kilroe pointed out that the water in Mullins' well varied with rainfall and probably collected initially in the porous glacial deposits through which the well passed. He suggested that Mullins had either sited his well right over a fault or over a tight fold of porous grit in the impermeable slate. In either case the structure – fault or fold – was serving as an outlet channel for the rainwater collected by the glacial deposits.

In the course of his career, John Mullins is said to have found more than 5,000 sources of water in the British Isles, for the landed gentry and others. His company's list of satisfied clients reads like an extract from *Burke's Peerage*. They included the contemporary Dukes of Westminster, Roxburgh, Sutherland, Marlborough, Rutland, Beaufort and Grafton; the Marquises of Salisbury, Exeter, Bristol and Bath, as well as nine earls and fourteen viscounts and barons.[17] During the latter part of his life, as well as his dowsing work, Mullins also ran a well-sinking company. He operated this on a money-back basis: if sufficient water was not found on the site indicated by his twig, Mullins would make no charge for the expensive sinking of the well. That Mullins could operate his business profitably on this basis is perhaps the best testament of all to the man's remarkable abilities as a water finder.

As a result of the professionalism of John Mullins and a few other dowsers of the Victorian period, many British scientists adopted an open-minded attitude to the ancient art. Though they had no idea how it worked, the scientists were forced to concede that some water dowsers had a surprisingly high success rate.

This favourable impression of dowsing was reinforced in the first half of the present century, when a succession of German and British official or military dowsers built up remarkable reputations as water finders. The first of these was the Prussian Landrat (magistrate) von Uslar.[18] Having established a solid dowsing record in Germany, von Uslar was sent by Kaiser Wilhelm II to South West Africa to find water for farmsteads in the arid German colony. During the period 1906–1908, von Uslar was so successful that the German Minister for the Colonies, Dr Dernburg, paid public tribute to his work in the Reichstag, mentioning that 81 per cent of the dowser's well sites had yielded sufficient water.

Another such dowser was the German army officer, Major Otto Edler von Graeve. After making a name for himself in Germany, when World War I broke out von Graeve was posted to the Middle East territories of the Ottoman Empire where he established a legendary reputation as a water finder. He used a stiff iron rod which moved with such force that it often broke the buttons of his uniform. On one occasion, reported by a sceptical German consul who had accompanied von Graeve on an expedition, the officer sited two excellent wells in a desert region where water had never been found within 20 kilometres.[19]

Then, in the 1920s, a British officer in the Indian Army – Major Charles Aubrey Pogson, of the Fifth Royal Mahrattas – came up with an even more impressive series of dowsing achievements.[20] In 1925 there was a drought and famine in the region of

Bombay. By then Pogson had already acquired a considerable local reputation as a dowser and the Legislative Council of the province took the extraordinary step of requesting the British Secretary of State for India that Pogson be appointed official Water Diviner to the Government of Bombay. Pogson held this post from 1925 to 1928, during which time he was responsible for providing water supplies to farms and villages in the most chronically drought-stricken areas.

The region where Pogson worked, near the towns of Ahmadnagar, Sholapur and Bijapur, lies on an immense pile of basalt lava flows, known as the Deccan Traps. These lavas poured out from countless volcanic vents millions of years ago as India moved northward before colliding with Asia to form the mighty Himalayas. As in many other areas of volcanic rock, even in times of normal rainfall, water can be difficult to find in the Deccan Traps. The rain-water quickly disappears into cracks in the rock, and can then only be found in such places as joints or fissures in the lavas or in the old soil horizons between the lava flows.

The idea that a water dowser could succeed where experts had failed seemed ludicrous to many people and the Bombay Legislative Council faced heavy criticism for creating the post of official dowser. But Pogson was soon able to silence the critics by the sheer quality of his work. Within the first year of his official duties he had already achieved a remarkable success rate. The *Indian Journal of Engineering* reported 'Major Pogson can find water, it appears, when the machines specially designed for the purpose have failed. It is an interesting situation. Out of 49 wells which have been sunk upon spots indicated by Major Pogson only two have failed to produce water. It is a notable achievement'. The London *Times* (30 April 1926) was also impressed. 'When the Bombay Legislative Council was sitting recently there was much criticism of the Government's appointment of Major Pogson as a water diviner. The facts now published show how successful Major Pogson has been and how fully he has justified his appointment at a high salary.'

During the three years that he held his official post, Pogson found water at 465 sites, 199 of them suitable for drinking and the remainder for irrigation purposes, an impressive record indeed.

Excellent though it was, however, Pogson's water-finding record in India would probably not convince a determined sceptic. Such a critic could argue that a geologist working under precisely the same conditions might have performed just as well or even better than the dowser. To impress the sceptic, what was needed was a demonstration that wells sited by a dowser could yield, on average, more water than those sited by geologists working in the same area.

About thirty years after Pogson's exploits in Bombay, another British dowser set himself the task of amassing data that would make just such a comparison possible. This time, though, the location was in Africa rather than India and the dowser was not a soldier but a retired colonial official: my father, Andrew Williamson.

My father first became an enthusiastic dowser after watching a French Roman Catholic missionary searching for water in the African bush with a forked mango stick. After learning what he could about the technique from people such as the British dowsing researcher Cecil Maby, and the distinguished Dutch geologist, Dr Solco Tromp – whose own dowsing investigations will be discussed later on – my father spent some years developing his own methods before working professionally.

The region he chose to work in was the border area between Kenya and Tanzania on the high plateau of East Africa. Underlying this part of Africa are ancient crystalline rocks of the kind that are found all over the continent. But this region happens to lie over a particularly hot part of the Earth's interior. Heating from below has forced the rocks to expand upwards and sideways, producing the great rift valleys and volcanoes that give East Africa its scenic splendour.

In this part of Africa the rainfall is seasonal and during much of the year rivers and streams dry up. Farmers are always seeking new supplies of underground water and this gave my father the opportunity to set up as a professional dowser in the tradition of Mullins and Pogson. Like a number of other professional dowsers he worked on a money-back basis: if a minimum specified quantity of water was not found before the drillers reached a specified depth, he returned the dowsing fee to his client.

My father was often remarkably successful. For instance, once he was called in to find water for a farm in Kenya, about 60 kilometres east of Nairobi. His whalebone rod reacted strongly at a site where the crystalline basement rocks were thinly covered with volcanic lavas and ash. The farmer then asked a government geologist to report on the site. He conducted a geophysical survey which confirmed that the site was a suitable one. After drilling for 60 metres, mainly through the crystalline basement, not a drop of water was found. The farmer was on the verge of giving up, but on my father's advice, decided to continue. Progress was slow at first, but then, at a depth of 73 metres, the drill suddenly broke through into the kind of decomposed rock that indicates the presence of a fracture zone. The hole yielded about 50 litres per minute, providing the farmer with a much-needed watering point for his cattle.

On a second occasion, another cattle ranch in the same area east of Nairobi required water. The farmer had had at least three holes drilled on sites selected by geologists, but all without success. So the farmer asked my father to locate a site by dowsing. After drilling 67 metres through the crystalline basement rock at my father's site, a small supply of water was found. My father advised his client to continue drilling and at 134 metres an excellent supply – 106 litres per minute – was found.

Later on, a good water supply was needed for the town of Arusha, in northern Tanzania. The town council had already drilled on two sites selected by a geologist on the slopes of Mount Meru, the great volcano that overshadows the town. Both holes were dry. So in desperation the council decided to drill on a site chosen by my father. This turned out to be a triumphant success: the well yielded more water than any available pump could cope with.

On another site near Arusha, however, the tables were turned against my father. The manager of a sisal estate needed an abundant supply of water and called in two water finders, a government geologist and my father, both of whom chose locations on volcanic lavas and ashes only a few hundred metres apart. The manager first drilled on my father's site but the driller encountered a series of gas pockets which forced him to abandon the hole at 105 metres. Then he drilled on the geologist's site: an excellent supply of water was found.

After five years of locating borehole sites for farmers and obtaining the reports on the subsequent drilling by the companies concerned my father had enough data to answer the crucial question – within a given area, do dowsed wells yield more water than those sited by geologists? The evidence was conclusive.[21] For boreholes drilled in volcanic rocks, 21 out of 25 wells located by my father yielded more than 100 gallons per hour (7.6 litres per minute). By contrast, only 6 out of 19 holes sited in these rocks by the Water Development Department of Tanganyika (later to become Tanzania) were similarly success-ful. What is more, while 7 out of the 25 holes located by my father were spectacular successes, yielding more than 3,000 gallons per hour (228 litres per minute), not one of those sited by the government geologists yielded as much.

The data also showed that my father was much better than the geologists at finding large supplies of water in the crystalline basement rocks. While only 6 per cent of the geologists' holes yielded more than 3,000 gallons per hour (228 litres per minute), no less than 23 per cent of my father's holes in the basement rocks yielded more than this amount.

While impressive, data collected in this way face an obvious criticism – a dowser is not the best person to assess his own work objectively. It would be better to have an independent account of a dowser's results compiled by a highly reputable organization.

An account of precisely this kind has recently become available in the form of reports prepared by the overseas technical aid agency of the German Government, the GTZ (*Deutsche Gesellschaft für Technische Zusammenarbeit*).[22, 23] They describe the remarkable exploits of the dowser Hans Schröter in Sri Lanka and other developing countries.

In common with people in other Third World countries, the villagers in the Vavuniya and Mullaitivu districts of north-east Sri Lanka suffer from various water-borne diseases. Many young babies die from gastroenteritis, while diarrhoea, infectious hepatitis and typhoid regularly claim the lives of numerous older people. In the past, the spread of these diseases was inevitable because the local people got their drinking water from shallow wells. These easily became contaminated with bacteria from human faeces – without access to latrines, most people had to defecate on the land surrounding their villages. The villagers' problems were even worse during the dry season, when the shallow wells ran dry and people had to get their water from the few public stand posts that were then available.

The German technical aid team saw that the way to solve the villagers' problems was to provide them with unpolluted water from deeper wells that would not run dry during droughts. But a major problem existed – good water supplies were difficult to find in the ancient crystalline rocks of the district. Like their counterparts in East Africa, these rocks only hold water in cracks and fissures with the most productive sources being fracture zones.

How, then, could the German team locate these water-bearing fracture zones? They tried several methods. They studied air photographs of the region to build up a picture of the local geology. They carried out electrical resistivity traverses – the geologists' favourite prospecting method for groundwater. They studied the vegetation for the clues it might provide. But by far the best method turned out to be dowsing, as practised by Hans Schröter, the project leader.

So successful were Schröter's initial dowsing surveys that the German team soon found that they were able to bring new wells on stream with remarkable efficiency. In each case, the team first got together with the villagers and identified possible well sites. To do this, they took into account the local geography and geology, the sites of existing wells, possible sources of contamination and – most important of all – accessibility to the village women who would actually have to fetch the water. Then Schröter carried out his dowsing survey, using a traditional forked rod. The dowser's performance must have greatly intrigued the villagers, particularly when the rod suddenly twisted, disclosing a suitable site. Finally, the team marked the location with a wooden peg and appointed a villager to look after the site until the drilling team arrived.

After drilling and fitting the well casing, the driller carried out pumping tests to find out the yield of each well. During pumping, the level of water in the well drops until enough water from the surrounding rocks percolates into the well to maintain the water at a lower level. The results of the tests were remarkable. Not only were there very few failures, but the average yield of the wells was in the range of 25 to 30 litres per minute, considerably better than expected. Altogether, 604 out of 657 wells drilled on the sites dowsed by Schröter were successful. Of the 57 apparent failures, the GTZ reported that 10 wells were dry because someone had moved the peg away from the dowsed site before drilling, and 16 wells had been destroyed by vandals. Only 27 of the 657 wells were real failures in the sense that the water at the dowsed site failed to meet the specified standards of quantity or quality.

As soon as testing had been completed, each of the wells was fitted with a hand pump and placed in the care of a villager – usually a woman – who was trained to maintain it. The availability of large quantities of pure water has transformed the lives of many thousands of villagers in this part of Sri Lanka though, tragically, a number of the wells were later put out of action as a result of the continuing ethnic conflict in the island.

Despite these problems, however, the way in which Schröter's dowsing enabled such a large number of wells to be brought on stream in a relatively short time made the Sri Lanka drinking water project one of the most successful ventures ever undertaken by the German technical aid agency. To achieve such results, Schröter must have sited a high proportion of his wells on the fracture zones in the crystalline rock.

The managers of the German technical aid agency were so impressed by Hans Schröter's work in Sri Lanka that they have since employed him as a sort of international troubleshooter.[24, 25] Wherever conventional water-finding methods have failed, the organization has flown Schröter in to sort things out. In each case the problem has been one of

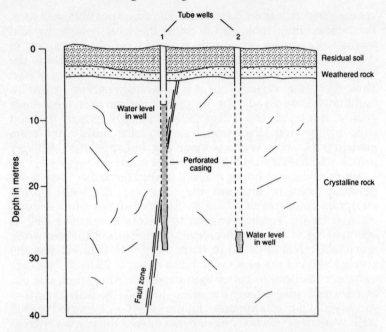

Fig.1 This demonstrates how a good dowser like Hans Schröter can find water in impermeable crystalline rock while a geologist may fail. Well 1, chosen by a dowser or geophysicist, taps water flowing in a hidden fault zone and yields plentiful water throughout the year. Well 2, chosen by a geologist without the aid of a dowser or geophysicist only taps water within a few cracks and joints and is almost dry

geology; the flow of suitable groundwater being confined to fracture zones, fissures or solution channels in limestone.

In the Dominican Republic in the Caribbean, for instance, Schröter located fracture zones that, when drilled, later yielded abundant mineral water with commercial potential as well as satisfactory drinking water. In another GTZ project, drinking water supplies were needed for many small communities near Kinkala, in the People's Republic of Congo. Because of the local limestone karst terrane, groundwater flowed only in channels that had proved difficult to locate with conventional methods. But Schröter, with his dowsing rod, has achieved spectacular results. By the summer of 1989, of 47 holes drilled, 29 yielded more than 40 litres per minute of drinking water, while 42 yielded adequate supplies of 5 litres per minute or more – a success rate of 90 per cent.[26]

Like several dowsers before him, Schröter's skills as a troubleshooter have proved particularly valuable in areas underlain by recent volcanic lavas and ash. For instance, communities in the volcanic Philippine island of Verde required underground supplies of fresh drinking water, not contaminated by salty water from the sea. Such fresh water flowed in systems of narrow fissures that had proved difficult to locate with conventional methods. Schröter, however, was able to pinpoint sites that yielded good supplies of drinking water.

On another occasion, Schröter was called upon to help locate well sites for a town in Wadi Ayyan, Yemen, between the ancient city of Sanaa and the Red Sea. The underlying rocks consisted of a volcanic sequence together with some sediments. Hydrogeologists working with the German aid agency used geophysical methods to delineate general areas for drilling, but left Schröter, with his dowsing rod, to choose the precise sites. This proved a wise decision, for when pump tested, the dowser's three wells yielded good supplies of 480, 780, and 1500 litres per minute.[27]

In recent years, Hans Schröter has also found good water supplies in the Cape Verde Islands (Fogo), Niger and Kenya. At the time of writing (mid 1992) he is performing wonders with his V-rod in Namibia, his results agreeing well with those of electromagnetic water-finding methods. Taken together with all his previous achievements in locating fracture zones and other water-bearing structures, this never-ending run of success makes Schröter one of the most remarkable water dowsers of all time, a worthy successor to the Baroness de Beausoleil, Barthelemy Bléton and John Mullins.

3   Dowsing, Earth Rays and Cancer

The notion that water can kill us sounds absurd. Nevertheless, this disturbing concept is probably as old as dowsing itself. For generations of dowsers have claimed that certain water-filled fissures or mineral veins emit harmful 'Earth rays' that may cause people living above to fall ill and die.

Another strange property of underground water, dowsers believed, was its power to attract thunderbolts. German dowsing folklore is replete with stories of trees growing over underground water being struck by lightning.[1, 2]

One of the first scientists to take the dowsers' concept of noxious Earth rays seriously was Pierre Cody, an engineer who, in the 1930s, lived in the French seaport of Le Havre.[3] Local dowsers told him of houses in the port where many people had died of cancer over the years.

Cody decided to investigate. If there really was energetic, noxious radiation in the 'cancer houses', it might be expected to cause ionization of the air and this could be detected by means of gold-leaf electroscopes. These consisted of a pair of thin gold leaves suspended from an electrical conductor attached to the outside of an insulating box. The operator first charges the gold leaves, causing them to repel each other and stand apart. Under normal conditions the leaves thereafter collapse very slowly. But if the operator places the electroscope in ionized air, the ions conduct charge away from the gold leaves, which quickly collapse. The greater the ionization of the air, the faster the leaves collapse.

Using electroscopes of this kind, Pierre Cody made measurements in various rooms of Le Havre houses where people had died of cancer. After checking a large number of dwellings Cody concluded that air in the so-called 'cancer houses' was ionized to an unusual degree.

What kind of 'Earth rays' or emanation had affected the air in this way? The emanation certainly behaved oddly. Cody found it – albeit in smaller quantities – in upper storeys of buildings as well as the lower ones. The amount of radiation seemed to increase with temperature, not only showing a daily variation, but also a seasonal one, being feeblest in winter and rising to a maximum in autumn. From various other tests Cody concluded that the ionizing radiation consisted of alpha particles. These positively charged particles, each consisting of two protons and two neutrons, can travel only a few centimetres in air. Because the particles were found almost everywhere in the 'cancer houses', they could have only come from a pervasive gas. There was only one gas known to emit alpha particles – radon.

To make sure that the ultimate cause of the air ionization was radon, Cody experimented with activated carbon. He found that the carbon would first absorb the emanation and later re-emit it, ionizing the air in the electroscope. Only radon could show this behaviour.

Pierre Cody's discovery of the radioactive gas in the 'cancer houses' of Le Havre solved the mystery of why, over the years, many of their occupants had died. For it is now known that radon is one of the most dangerous substances known. The gas consists of several isotopes – atoms with nuclei containing the same numbers of protons but different numbers of neutrons. The greatest danger comes from radon-222, which has 86 protons and 136 neutrons. This isotope has a half-life of about 3.8 days: decaying to polonium-218 by shooting off an energetic alpha particle. When we breathe the gas into our lungs, some of the radon-222 atoms behave like miniature cannons, bombarding the cells there with their tiny alpha projectiles.

But even after the radon-222 atoms have fired their alpha particles, there is more to come. The newly formed polonium-218 atoms decay very quickly to other 'daughters'; as they decay each atom first ejects another alpha particle and then a series of high-speed electrons and high-energy gamma rays. All these events further damage the cells of our lungs and other organs, increasing our chances of succumbing to cancer.

To make matters worse, any room containing radon will also contain polonium-218 and the other daughters as aerosols suspended in the air. So the air breathed by anyone in the room is polluted not only by radon-222 itself, but also by the radioactivity of its many daughters. In the light of all this, it is not surprising that over the years so many people had died in the houses where Pierre Cody found high levels of radon.

Pierre Cody's careful demonstration that the radioactive gas was present in some Le Havre 'cancer houses' showed that there might after all be some truth in the dowsers' traditional concept of noxious Earth rays. Intriguingly, the radon idea could also make sense of the folklore belief that lightning was attracted to places over water-bearing fissures. Radon dissolved in underground water might ionize the air above which could then provide a path for lightning strikes just as an ordinary lightning conductor does.

But was radon gas the only component of the harmful emanations? Some dowsers – including Cody himself – believed that people's health could also be harmed by beams of penetrating radiation rising from the ground. An obvious possibility was gamma radiation – the penetrating rays emitted by many radioactive isotopes including some of the radon daughters. This idea was later explored by Dr Joseph Wüst, a German scientist who devoted much time to dowsing research and Jakob Stängle, a German engineer and dowser.[4, 5]

Working in the 1950s with a Geiger counter – a development of the simple electroscope used by Cody – Wüst found unusually large amounts of gamma radiation in the rooms of cancer patients in the German town of Pleutersbach. Then, in the 1970s, Jakob Stängle carried out further investigations with the aid of a scintillation counter, an even more sophisticated instrument that detects the light flashes or scintillations emitted by a crystalline sensor when penetrated by ionizing radiation.

Stängle, who had a very good record of locating water-bearing fissures in crystalline rock, claimed that such fissures often emitted unusually large amounts of gamma radiation. Could these fissures be a significant cause of cancer? Stängle carried out a survey with his scintillation counter in the town of Moulins, north of Clermont-Ferrand in France. A local physician, Dr J. Picard, had claimed that cancer victims in the town had often dwelt above geological fractures. For instance, in one house a 12-year-old boy developed a sarcoma and died. Another family then moved into the same house and their 9-year-old son slept in the same bedroom as the 12-year-old boy. The 9-year-old, too, developed a fatal sarcoma.

Stängle wheeled his scintillation counter through the streets outside the house where the two boys had died. He found high levels of gamma radiation, which he believed came from water-bearing fractures. Stängle further claimed that the levels of gamma radiation were also high in the vicinity of other 'cancer houses' in Moulins.

While Cody, Wüst and Stängle thought that the gamma radiation from fissures could be a significant cause of cancer, more recent scientific knowledge suggests that this is unlikely.[6, 7] Because they tend to whizz right through us, gamma rays do less damage to our bodies than the alpha particles from radon. In any case, we are constantly bombarded by gamma rays from radioactive isotopes such as potassium-40 that are present in most building materials. So the extra dose from any fissures or fractures that may be beneath our houses is not likely to do us much harm.

But could such fissures emit other forms of ionizing radiation that might be carcinogenic? Following in the footsteps of Wüst and Stängle, a third German researcher, Wolfgang Maes, has recently developed a supersensitive scintillation counter that is claimed to detect another kind of penetrating radiation – fast neutrons.[8] Using such instruments, Maes claims that certain water-bearing fissures and fractures emit intense beams of these short-lived, high-velocity particles – presumably released from local atoms hit by alpha particles from radon. Though, like gamma rays, fast neutrons tend to shoot right through our bodies, a few score bull's-eye hits on atomic nuclei within us, the resulting damage doing us no good at all.

Because the idea is such a novel one, the possibility that beams of fast neutrons from water-bearing fissures may be a significant cause of cancer has not yet been confirmed. At the moment, it still seems likely that it is chiefly by emitting radon that water-bearing fissures and fractures may damage our health. If ionizing radiation did play a part in the tragic deaths of the two boys in Moulins, alpha radiation from radon and its daughters seems likely to have been the culprit.

The labours of Pierre Cody and the three German researchers therefore make it possible to express the traditional dowsers' claim in the following terms: certain mineral veins, water-bearing fissures and geological fractures emit the deadly radioactive gas, radon, thereby posing a significant cancer risk to people living above.

This claim is a staggeringly important one. If true, it offers prospects for preventing many thousands, perhaps millions, of people from becoming victims of the disease feared most by twentieth-century Westerners. For, as we shall see later, there are ways of stopping the killer gas from entering our homes.

Until very recently, however, orthodox scientists and physicians entirely ignored the dowsers' claim, despite the new evidence that was starting to support it. They continued to dismiss the whole concept of carcinogenic water-bearing fissures (termed geopathic zones by Johannes Walther, a German geologist, in 1933) as utter nonsense.

To be fair to orthodoxy, the scientific establishment had some good reasons to regard this idea with suspicion. For if people like Pierre Cody and Joseph Wüst had shown a commendably scientific approach to the subject, others had marched to the beat of a different drum. The most influential of these enthusiasts was a rather eccentric German aristocrat, Baron Gustav von Pohl.

Like many another of his kind, the Baron was certain that he was the sole possessor of a great truth. All illness and disease, the Baron held, whether of animals or human beings, had one simple explanation: Earth currents. Whether a patient was suffering from insomnia or rheumatism, cancer or tuberculosis, the cause, the Baron explained, was an electric current running through the ground beneath the unfortunate person's bed. When asked how he knew this, the Baron had to admit that unlike other electric currents, his electric currents could not be detected by any instrument known to man. Fortunately, though, the Baron himself could detect the currents – by dowsing.[9]

Convinced that he alone could, by dowsing, discern the aetiology of all the illness in the world, Baron von Pohl became a very busy man indeed. Unable to solve all the world's medical problems at a stroke, this latter-day Hippocrates decided to start with the Bavarian town of Vilsbiburg. Accompanied by the mayor or one of his deputies, on a bleak January day in 1929 the Baron marched through the streets of the town, his dowsing rod twitching furiously in apparent response to the electric currents flowing below. After seven days of frenzied dowsing, Baron von Pohl had enough information to compile his results. He drew up a map looking rather like a plate of half-eaten spaghetti, but which, according to the Baron, showed all the carcinogenic electric currents as they twisted and turned beneath Vilsbiburg.

Then Baron von Pohl compared the positions of his Earth currents with the locations of houses where, according to death certificates, people had died of cancer in the previous ten years. He claimed that an electric current ran beneath the bed of each cancer victim in Vilsbiburg.

The Vilsbiburg survey marked only the beginning of the Baron's campaign to rid the world of disease. He surveyed the smaller Bavarian town of Grafenau and again found an electric current below the bed of every cancer victim. Unable to cope with the growing demand for his services, the Baron taught other dowsers how to find Earth currents. Soon many people were claiming to confirm the Baron's findings. In the city of Stettin, for example, a certain Dr Hager, chairman of the city's medical scientific association, asserted that underground electric currents ran beneath the beds of all 5,348 people who had died of cancer during a twenty-one-year period.[10]

Baron von Pohl was bitterly disappointed that the scientific world did not immediately accept his claim that all ill health was caused by Earth currents. But his disciples continued to practise his unorthodox methods. Their therapeutic techniques could hardly be simpler. Whatever the illness or problem was, the diagnosis and treatment were always the same. As the cause of the malady was always an electric current beneath the patient's bed, the solution was to move the bed to another part of the room. If we are to believe the accounts written by the Baron and his disciples this treatment was always successful.

Baron von Pohl's claims were so preposterous that it is hard to see why anyone should have taken them seriously. But quite remarkably, his ideas not only survived, but more than sixty years on are more popular than ever. Instead of Earth currents though, contemporary devotees of this cult believe that bands of noxious radiation rise vertically from the ground. The bed movers, who call themselves geobiologists, say that these bands of radiation – which they claim to detect by dowsing – intersect to form grid-like networks that cover the whole surface of the Earth. They treat all illness by moving the patients' beds away from the alleged radiation bands.

The popularity of Baron von Pohl's daft bed-moving cult led most scientists to view the whole subject of dowsing, Earth rays and cancer as so much nonsense. Orthodox scientists overlooked the careful work by Pierre Cody, Joseph Wüst and Jakob Stängle supporting the traditional dowsers' claim that some water-filled fissures, mineral veins and geological fractures really do emit a noxious emanation – radon.

It is true that scientists were aware of the health risks posed by radon, but most considered it a minor problem, limited to a few localized areas and in no way connected with the dowsers' crazy idea of geopathic zones. It was not until the late 1980s that the scientific world began to realize the full extent of the threat that the gas posed to our health.

A crucial event that shattered the scientists' complacency happened on 2 December 1984 at the Limerick nuclear power station near Philadelphia in the USA.[11] Like other nuclear power stations, the Limerick plant was fitted with alarms designed to go off in the event of radioactivity rising to dangerous levels. On that winter morning, the alarms did go off, but nobody could find out why. The technical staff checked again and again, but could discover no leakage of radiation that could have triggered the alarms.

The next morning exactly the same thing happened again. The alarms sounded, quite inexplicably. They continued to go off every morning, driving the staff mad with anxiety. Finally, after two weeks of mounting tension, the technical staff found out what was happening. One of the power station's employees, Stanley Watras, was so radioactive that he was triggering the alarm each morning as he walked into work.

It turned out that Stanley Watras's house, in a community nearby called Boyertown, had been built on a 10-metre wide

excavated vein of uranium ore. Radon from the vein had seeped
into his house. The deadly gas was so concentrated that in each
cubic metre of air in the house 100,000 atoms were exploding
each second and firing off their lethal alpha bullets. This
concentration of 100,000 becquerels per cubic metre must have
been giving Stanley Watras a yearly radiation dose of about
2,000 millisieverts – as bad for his health as if he smoked 135
packets of cigarettes a day.

Some people might think that Stanley Watras's case history
conclusively vindicated dowsers' claims concerning geopathic
zones. But orthodox scientists could still argue that his was a
very special case. The dangers of radiation from uranium ore
were well known, they could point out, and it was not
surprising that someone unfortunate enough to live directly
above a uranium-bearing vein would be at risk. There was little
need for most of us to worry.

The spectacular circumstances of Stanley Watras's case
nevertheless did help to make the US authorities take the radon
problem more seriously. The Environmental Protection Agency
started to conduct national surveys of radon levels in·houses. In
the United Kingdom, the National Radiological Protection Board
did likewise. These large-scale surveys were made possible by
the existence of simple and cheap radiation monitors. These are
basically pots containing material that records tracks of alpha
particles emitted by radon and its daughters. In the course of the
surveys people were asked to keep these pots in various rooms
of their houses: after suitable periods the pots were removed
and the number of tracks counted in a laboratory.

The first results of these national surveys were profoundly
disturbing. Instead of being confined, as predicted, to small
areas of uranium-rich rocks, high levels of radon seemed to be
far more widespread. In the USA, the investigators found
dangerously high levels of radon in thousands of houses. For
instance, a long belt of high radon activity stretched from a point
about 50 kilometres north of New York city to the town of
Reading, Pennsylvania – just south-west of Boyertown, where
Stanley Watras lived. Altogether the results suggested that in
one in eight American homes, people were breathing air
dangerously contaminated by radon.[12]

In the United Kingdom, the findings were equally alarming.[13]
Before the survey, most specialists thought that the problem of
radioactive air would be confined to a few houses only, chiefly
those built on the granite rocks of Cornwall, Devon and
Scotland. But the results painted a very different picture. The
researchers found high concentrations of radon in many areas
where there were no uranium-rich granites at all. For example,

they discovered dangerously high levels of radon in Somerset, Derbyshire, Yorkshire and Northamptonshire as well as in Cornwall and Devon. In January 1990, the National Radiological Protection Board estimated that people in some 90,000 British homes were breathing air contaminated to a level of 200 becquerels per cubic metre or more and were therefore receiving yearly radiation doses of at least 10 millisieverts.

The devastating effects of such widespread radiation on human health can be brought out by comparing the size of the radon hazard with that experienced by workers at nuclear power stations or reprocessing plants. In Britain, for example, there has for a number of years been extreme public concern about the health risks presented by the Sellafield (formerly Windscale) nuclear reprocessing plant in Cumbria. In February 1990, this reached a crescendo with the publication of a study by a team at Britain's Medical Research Council suggesting that children of workers at Sellafield were more likely to develop leukaemia than other children. The team found that children of workers who had been exposed to a radiation dose of 10 millisieverts or more in the six months prior to conception faced a six- to eight-fold increase in their risk of developing leukaemia. In a subsequent interview with Alan Franks of *The Times* newspaper[14] Christopher Harding, Chairman of British Nuclear Fuels Limited (BNFL), said that in 1988 443 workers at Sellafield received an annual dose of more than 15 millisieverts, of whom only two received more than 50 millisieverts. Britain's Health and Safety Executive had recommended that BNFL adopt a maximum permitted dose of 15 millisieverts within a year.

But how many ordinary British people receive annual radiation doses of more than 15 millisieverts as a result of breathing radioactive air in their own 'cancer houses'? The answer is chilling. Th NRPB's work would suggest that at least 100,000 British people receive more than 15 millisieverts annually, and of these, thousands are exposed to more than 50 millisieverts. In other words, for every Sellafield worker whose health – or children's health – is at risk from radiation, perhaps a thousand more of us are receiving equally dangerous doses in our own homes.

Some people make light of the radon threat by arguing that the deadly gas is a natural and immutable hazard of life we must all accept. This is simply not true. If we lived in the open, like our African ancestors, radon would hardly trouble us. For it is our houses that are to blame. Modern Western-style homes, with their underfloor service conduits, central heating, draught proofing and double glazing are actually high-technology radiation traps. The combination of heating and draught proofing means that the air pressure inside the house tends to be slightly lower than the pressure outside. As a result, any radon in the ground beneath is sucked up through small cracks and crevices into the home.

Fortunately for those at risk, research centres such as the Building Research Establishment at Watford in England are developing ways of treating potential 'cancer houses' to make them safer.[15] For example, floors can be sealed to prevent the radon seeping in and extractor fans can be fitted to suck the radon away from the underfloor area and discharge it harmlessly outside. In Sweden, the National Institute for Building Research has developed a method in which radon is sucked out from as much as a hectare of soil and discharged into the air before it reaches house foundations.

So relatively cheap methods are already available to prevent people from being exposed to dangerous levels of radioactivity in their own homes. The crucial question, of course, is which homes are at risk? The NRPB's estimate that people living in about 90,000 British households receive annual radiation doses of more than 10 millisieverts is a very crude assessment based on a limited number of measurements. Governments in Britain and elsewhere have not yet given their radiation protection authorities sufficient resources to pinpoint precisely which dwellings are likely to be 'cancer houses'.

Could the dowsers' concept of geopathic zones help in identifying the high-risk houses? As we have already seen, generations of dowsers have claimed that houses above certain water-bearing fissures and fracture zones are unsafe. If this idea is correct, it would be invaluable in deciding which houses should be tested for radon.

To see if the concept of geopathic zones really could have a sound scientific basis, we need some understanding of the history of radon's ultimate source, uranium-238. Like other heavy isotopes, uranium-238 was created from lighter atoms inside exploding stars known as supernovae billions of years ago. As the explosions took place, so many neutrons were flying around that some uranium atoms ended up with as many as 146 of them – more than they could cope with. Ever since, these uranium-238 atoms have been trying to revert to more stable configurations with fewer neutrons. In the first, slow, step in this process, the uranium nucleus emits an alpha particle, followed quickly by two electrons. Once they have started to decay, uranium-238 atoms produce a chain of daughters, including radium-226, the parent of radon-222.

The material that accreted to form the Earth about 4,500 million years ago included some uranium-238 atoms. During the long and complex history of the Earth's crust, the slowly disintegrating uranium-238 atoms became concentrated in certain rocks such as granites and clays. It is these concentrations of decaying uranium atoms that are the ultimate cause of the radon hazard.

These ideas make it easy to see why scientists at first thought that the amount of radon seeping into our houses would simply depend on the uranium content of the rocks beneath. In fact, as we have seen, surveys carried out by radiological protection authorities have shown that the truth is far more complicated. The key factor seems to be not so much the uranium content of the rock but whether or not radon, with a half-life of only 3.8 days, can escape to the surface before it decays.

The first clues to support the new thinking on radon came from studies in mines. The largest amounts of radon were found not in uranium mines but at particular sites in other mines. Investigations showed that these 'hot spots' were places where geological faults and fractures allowed ground water to enter the mine workings – just the places where the miners of old first started to dowse for 'water veins'.

These mine investigations provide some support for the dowsers' scorned concept of geopathic zones. But recently, even more evidence has accumulated to substantiate the dowsers' traditional belief that harmful emanations – which we can now identify as radon – are particularly associated with water-bearing fissures. The new support came from measurements of the radon activity in water samples collected from streams.

The underlying principle of this technique is that the radon content of a small stream reflects the average groundwater radon level in the stream's source area. In effect such streams do much of the time-consuming sampling work for the investigators: all the researchers need do is collect and measure the radon in water samples from suitable streams. In this way, investigators can draw up maps showing the radon content of groundwater locally in some detail. For example, Eric Durrance, of the University of Exeter, has carried out a stream water radon survey of the area around the Carnmenellis granite in Cornwall.[16] The concentration of radon in groundwater showed a surprisingly large variation in localities only a short distance apart. The radon concentrations depended not so much on the nature of the rocks below – granite or slate – as on the presence of fractures cutting through the rock. Radon levels in the neighbourhood of north-west-trending fractures were many times greater than those in other areas.

How then can we explain the fact that certain water-bearing fissures are associated with dangerously high levels of radon?

Several factors may be involved. But one key appears to lie in the way that the fissures can channel rising radon-rich groundwater. In many regions of crystalline rock, including the granites of south-west England, the rocks contain enough decaying uranium-238 and other radioactive isotopes to heat the water derived from rain as it sinks deep into the rock. When it warms up, the water expands and begins to rise towards the top of the water table. As it seeps through the cracks and fissures in the rocks, the rising groundwater picks up not only radon's parent, radium-226, but also radon gas itself. The water rising along fissures and fractures is therefore charged with radon, which may then seep out of the ground and into our homes.

One question remains. If, as dowsers have long maintained and the scientific evidence now confirms, the carcinogenic gas radon does rise up along certain water-bearing faults, fractures and fissures, this effect should be detectable in medical records. Houses where people die of lung cancer should tend to cluster near geological faults and fracture zones.

In actual fact, however, the chances that a person will die of cancer depend not only on the concentration of radon in their house but also many other factors. In Britain, for instance, where about 50,000 people die of lung cancer each year, smoking claims the largest number of victims. According to the NRPB's 1990 estimate, radon is in second place, killing about 2,500 men, women and children each year. As well as smoking and radon, other environmental hazards, such as benzene in motor vehicle exhaust gases also cause lung cancer.

Such effects mean that anyone seeking to find out if 'cancer houses' do indeed cluster along geological faults and fissures would need to conduct a very sophisticated and costly epidemiological study. As the concept that unusually high domestic levels of radon are often associated with faults and fracture zones is only now becoming scientifically respectable, it is not surprising that few people have had the courage and resources to tackle this vitally important problem.

There are, however, at least two intriguing pieces of evidence linking cancer deaths with geological faults. In 1927 two German researchers, H. Winzer and W. Melzer, published a report on the distribution of cancer deaths in the city of Stuttgart. The city lies on sedimentary rocks – mostly sandstones, claystones and limestones. The rocks dip gently towards the south-east so that the oldest layers lie under the north-west part of Stuttgart. Several north-west trending faults cut across the city.

At first the researchers thought that the incidence of cancer might depend on the geological formation beneath. But no such correlation was found. So the researchers decided to investigate the dowsers' claim that there might be a link between the faults and the cancer deaths. To their surprise, this idea turned out to be correct. The faults ran through precisely those districts which had the highest cancer mortality.[17]

Another study suggesting that people living over certain fault zones are more likely than others to contract radon-mediated cancer was carried out in the 1970s in Romania.[18] Professor Geza Malnasi, of the Medical School at Tirgu Mures, and colleagues studied the incidence of cancer in the Gheorghieni Depression region of Transylvania, along the Mures valley. A major north-west-trending fault ran across the area, conducting mineral water charged with carbon dioxide and radon gases to the surface. Professor Malnasi and his team found the incidence of cancer in villages intersected by the fault to be 10–20 times higher than the average for the country.

Unfortunately for Malnasi, these results were not to the liking of the Ceausescu regime, then in control of Romania. Many of the villages in the fault zone were inhabited by Hungarian-speaking people. To find cancer clusters here was politically undesirable in that rumours of their existence might ignite the smouldering embers of ethnic conflict in the region. Professor Malnasi lost his job and was banished to northernmost Moldavia – the Romanian equivalent of the Siberian salt mines.

Though further investigations are urgently needed, these two epidemiological studies suggest that the dowsers of old may have been right after all. Certain water-bearing fissures, geological faults and fracture zones do indeed emit noxious emanations that can kill us, just as they said. People living in high-risk areas and concerned about the radon hazard could do far worse than seek geological advice as to whether or not the rocks beneath their houses are fractured and fissured.

Sadly, though, it has to be admitted that one thing people worried about radon should not do is to consult a dowsing society or group. Members of these numerous organizations – there are some seventeen in Britain alone – are likely to be followers of Baron von Pohl's bed-moving cult. These well-intentioned but deluded individuals believe that radiation risk may be avoided by moving a patient's bed to a different part of the room; some even claim to eliminate hazardous radiation by the use of devices such as copper coils or mysterious black boxes. Such pseudoscientific methods for treating potential 'cancer houses' are worse than useless. They give worried people the false impression that their radiation problem has been solved when in fact they may be continuing to receive dangerous doses of alpha-radiation from radon and its daughters.

The way in which many present-day 'Earth ray' dowsing enthusiasts have been led astray by pseudoscience should not obscure the fact that the dowsers of old showed a remarkable prescience in pointing out the harmful effects of certain water-bearing fissures. How did they do it?

One clue may lie in Georgius Agricola's 1556 observation[19] that the lungs of miners in the Erzgebirge Mountains were rotting away as a result of the 'pestilential air' they breathed. It is possible that the early dowsing miners of the Erzgebirge noticed that emanations from certain uranium-rich ore veins there caused lung disease. They may also have observed the bad health of those working in underground tunnels cut by water-bearing fissures. The miners may have concluded that both dowsable mineral lodes and 'water veins' emit harmful emanations. After the craft of mineral dowsing had died out in the nineteenth century, a memory of the link between certain 'water veins' and harmful Earth rays may have survived as part of German dowsing folklore.

4 A New Technique for Archaeologists?

When Napoleon invaded Russia in 1812, his 'Grande Armée' was opposed by the forces of General Kutuzov near the village of Borodino outside Moscow. To protect their artillery from the advancing French cavalry, the Russians dug networks of deep pits in the ground about 100 metres in front of their guns. They hoped that the French horses would stumble into the pits and break their legs.

Precisely how effective these so-called 'wolf-holes' were is a matter for military historians to decide. But their exact location was of considerable interest to the Russian officials who, in the 1970s, were trying to reconstruct the bloody battlefield as part of a programme to restore Soviet historical monuments. Since 1812 the battleground had been repeatedly ploughed up and trees had been planted in some areas. In the 1940s, another Moscow-bound invading army – that of Adolf Hitler – had provoked a second battle on the site. So, by the 1970s, all knowledge of the wolf-holes' exact positions had been lost.

How then could the Russian restoration workers locate the correct positions of the wolf-holes? Some time previously they had been intrigued by the dowsing exploits of Alexander Pluzhnikov, an engineer who had shown an apparently uncanny ability to trace the buried foundations of old buildings. So they asked him to see if he could locate the wolf-holes.

Pluzhnikov walked to and fro across the site of the old battlefield, clutching in each hand a special L-rod of his own design. According to a report written jointly by the dowser and two restoration archaeologists, and published by the Ministry of Culture of the Russian Soviet Socialist Republic, Pluzhnikov was remarkably accurate in predicting the places where the old wolf holes were later found by digging.[1] Not only that, the dowser reportedly discovered a large number of graves, some in the vicinity of the Russian battery and others near the command post of Napoleon himself. The Frenchmen's bodies had been arranged in ordered rows with their feet pointing north. The restorers believed that the graves contained the remains of

Napoleon's senior commanders who would have been buried with full military honours near the Emperor's headquarters.

Alexander Pluzhnikov's successful dowsing survey at Borodino was only one of several similarly well-documented contributions that he made to Soviet archaeology.[2] For instance on one occasion the dowser reportedly located the foundations of an old palace near the village of Bol'shye Vyazemy belonging to the sixteenth-century Russian Czar, Boris Godunov. Another of Pluzhnikov's exploits concerned the site of a fifteenth-century monastery cathedral near Moscow where restoration archaeologists had been working for many years. When Pluzhnikov arrived on the site, he was able to explain many of the features that had been puzzling the archaeologists. Thus old records suggested that at one time the cathedral had been connected by a passageway to a refectory for the monks. Using his special L-rods, Pluzhnikov is said to have correctly predicted the positions of ancient columns on either side of the passageway and also the outlines of a grave between the columns.

Alexander Pluzhnikov claimed not only to be able to detect features such as old foundations and graves, he could also, it seems, trace underground tunnels or cavities in the same manner as Barthelemy Bléton, the eighteenth-century French peasant who had dowsed for Marie Antoinette. The Soviet dowser demonstrated this apparent ability when dowsing in the old city of Serphukov, south of Moscow.

This city, sited at the point where the Nara River is joined by the Oka, was founded in the fourteenth century as a stronghold to protect Moscow from the Tatars. According to tradition, during the Middle Ages the townspeople dug tunnels to serve as hiding places or escape routes from the invading hordes. Using his L-rods, Pluzhnikov is reported to have traced a two-metre-wide tunnel network connecting the town's kremlin with two fortified monasteries. The tunnels appeared to pass under the River Nara in two places.

Despite these seemingly impressive achievements, Pluzhnikov was not able to convince the Soviet archaeological establishment of the value of his technique. This was a pity, because the claims of dowsers to detect buried foundations, graves, tunnels and the like are easier to test than their claims to locate underground water. When a dowser finds water, a sceptic can always put it down to chance. But when, like Pluzhnikov, a dowser repeatedly traces with accuracy the outlines of underground features such as graves or tunnels, even the most hardened critic would find it difficult to attribute all his results to chance.

Alexander Pluzhnikov is not the only dowser to have an

Mineral dowsers at work in sixteenth-century Germany. A man
cuts a dowsing rod from a tree in the distance, while in the
middle distance and foreground two dowsers (labelled 'A')
search for hidden veins of metal ore

Watched by three curious onlookers, the rod of a seventeenth-
century German dowser flips up as he approaches a concealed
mineral lode

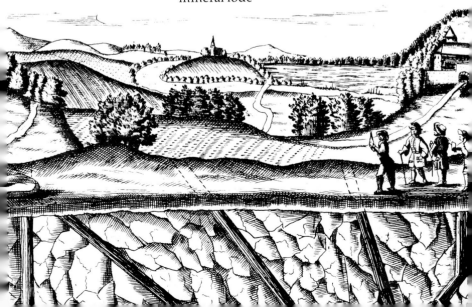

A team of dowsers locating cross-cutting mineral veins. A surveyor marks out the course of one dowsed vein, while two miners look on (1700)

William Pryce, a surgeon from Redruth, Cornwall, was one of the eighteenth-century's leading authorities on mining practice and a firm believer in the efficacy of dowsing

authenticated record of detecting underground tunnels and cavities. In 1913 the French biologist Dr Armand Viré, one time director of a laboratory at the National Museum of Natural History in Paris, tested several dowsers' claims in this respect. Viré was an expert on caves, having studied cave-dwelling and other underground animals in his laboratory below the Jardin des Plantes in Paris. A group of French scientists interested in dowsing approached this underground expert to ask if he would be interested in devising an experiment to see if dowsers really could locate underground tunnels and cavities.[3, 4]

After reflection, Viré concluded that underground Paris, with its vast network of passageways and workings, would make an excellent test for the dowsers. The subterranean features were only marked on an unpublished map that was kept under lock and key, obviating the possibility that the dowsers could find out the locations of the tunnels beforehand.

So Viré organized a test similar in some respects to the ones that had been devised for Barthelemy Bléton nearly a century and a half before. Using traditional forked rods, the dowsers walked over the grassy test site. Viré reported to the French Academy of Sciences that one dowser, a retired gendarme, correctly located the borders of an underground quarry. Another dowser, a Monsieur Probst, was apparently able to find the pillars of rock left by quarrymen to support the roof of their underground workings.

To take another well-documented report of dowsers correctly locating underground tunnels, there is the strange story of Louis Matacia and the US Marines.[5] In the mid-1960s the ingenuity and determination of the Viet Cong guerillas were creating immense difficulties for the American forces in Vietnam. Jungle villages that seemed to be securely in American control would turn out to be riddled with underground tunnels, hiding chambers for the guerillas and storerooms for weapons and supplies. To make matters worse, investigating soldiers were liable to fall into lethal booby traps known as punji pits. Beneath an apparently normal surface of soil and vegetation lay a pit containing two boards bearing steel spikes smeared with excrement. When the hapless soldier stumbled into the pit, the steel spiked boards would pivot and close on his legs, simultaneously wounding him and infecting the wounds.

The problem of detecting the Viet Cong's underground tunnels was so acute that Robert McNamara, then US Secretary of Defense, appealed for any new ideas that might help to solve it. At a meeting held at the US Marines Development and Educational Center at Quantico, Virginia in 1966, Louis Matacia, a land surveyor who was a consultant to the Marines suggested that they try dowsing. Matacia offered to demonstrate how to locate underground tunnels using the technique.

At their Development Center the Marines had constructed a model Viet Cong village, complete with underground tunnels, store chambers and even a punji trap. So a few days after the first meeting, assembled officers and men of the Marines assessed Matacia's assertion that he could locate the tunnels by dowsing. Using a pair of wire L-rods, Matacia surveyed the village, his rods swinging outwards when he experienced a dowsing response.

In later interviews with Christopher Bird, the American writer and dowsing enthusiast, Matacia claimed that on that day he did not make a single mistake in locating underground tunnels and other features of the hidden village. Making due allowance for the time-honoured propensity of dowsers to embellish accounts of their successes – and quickly forget their failures – Matacia's dowsing performance must at least have been impressive enough to make the Marines eager to use the technique. Very soon, Marines in Vietnam were dowsing with L-rods for hidden tunnels and caves. According to Bird, the American Commander-in-Chief in Vietnam himself sent positive reports about dowsing to the Marine Development Center at Quantico. The *New York Times* reported that engineer units of the 1st and 3rd US Marine Divisions were using L-rods to detect tunnels and caves with 'marked success'.

On 13 March 1967, *The Observer*, a weekly newspaper published in Saigon for American forces in Vietnam, reported that 'Matacia's Wire Rudders' were being used by Marines of the 2nd Battalion, 5th Marine Regiment. Although regarded with scepticism by many, the newspaper reported that Marines using the wire L-rods had found a few Viet Cong tunnels. The report continued:

> Private First Class Don R. Steiner, Shadyside, Ohio, a battalion scout with the 2nd Battalion, 1st Marine Regiment, tried the rods for the first time on a recent patrol. The rods spread apart as Steiner passed a Vietnamese hut.
> Upon checking inside the building, Marines discovered a tunnel that led to a family bunker underneath the trail, right where the rods had reacted.

While Marines dowsed unofficially in Vietnam, back in Quantico technical staff at the Marines Development Center attempted to evaluate Matacia's dowsing method. Acknowledging that in practice dowsing had been used with varying degrees of success, the technical staff could not come up with any theoretical explanation for the good results. Until the science behind dowsing had been unravelled, the commanding officer at Quantico stated, the Marine Corps could not adopt the method for official use by its units.

The US Marine Development Center's opinion that without supporting theory, dowsing's value is limited, coincides precisely with the views of the eighteenth-century European mining experts and the Soviet geological and archaeological authorities in the 1970s. On all three occasions, the authorities rejected dowsing not because it didn't work but because they couldn't explain it.

Despite the lack of official backing, evidence has continued to accumulate that some dowsers have an uncanny ability to locate features just below the surface of the ground. One such dowser, a retired engineer called Denis Briggs, has recently impressed the British archaeological establishment with a series of contributions to church archaeology.[6, 7, 8, 9]

The story began when Briggs approached Professor Richard Bailey, an expert in English church archaeology at the University of Newcastle-upon-Tyne, with a number of plans of local churches. The plans were exceptional for several reasons. They showed not only existing church walls but also the positions of ancient ones. Even more surprising was the way Briggs had prepared his plans. For instead of using conventional remote sensing equipment such as magnetometers, Briggs had carried out his surveys using nothing more elaborate than a pair of L-shaped dowsing rods.

Like most of his colleagues, Bailey was at first entirely sceptical about the idea that a dowser like Briggs really could detect archaeological remains below the ground surface. But he was intrigued by some of the features shown on the dowser's plans. They made sense in a way that only an expert in the history of English church architecture could understand.

If dowsing really worked, it would be a most useful alternative to conventional remote sensing equipment such as magnetometers and resistivity meters which have obvious disadvantages when used inside buildings such as churches. So Bailey decided to embark on a programme of verification to see how accurate Denis Briggs really was in locating subsurface features by dowsing.

Some of these turned out to be very frustrating exercises. On one occasion Briggs came up with a dowsed plan of Bedlington church. His plan showed a remarkable curved amphitheatre occupying the northern part of the present nave. When Bailey checked up on the old plans of the church in Northumberland Record Office, he found that before 1912 an amphitheatre corresponding closely to the one indicated on the dowser's plan had indeed existed. Moreover there seemed no possibility that Briggs had obtained his information from the Public Record Office, as, according to Bailey, the dowser had completed his plan before consulting the documents in the Record Office.

However, as Bailey himself points out, a sceptic would naturally suspect that Denis Briggs had found out about the old amphitheatre from some source or other before completing his dowsed plan. Only a true believer would accept this story as evidence that dowsing really works.

In other instances, Bailey tried to verify the dowser's predictions by digging. One of the churches that Denis Briggs had surveyed with his L-rods was a priory at Hexham, dating from the thirteenth century. The dowser predicted that a series of underground features would be found, running northwards beneath the western portion of the chapter-house vestibule attached to the priory. In 1984 Eric Cambridge, an archaeological colleague of Bailey's at the University of Durham, excavated part of the vestibule's floor. To his surprise, he found a substantial mortared foundation in almost exactly the position predicted by Briggs.

But was this really such a triumphant vindication of dowsing as it seemed? Bailey admits that the existence of a foundation beneath the vestibule had been known for many years; moreover plans of the mediaeval structures in the church had been published on several occasions. So, again, it was possible that Briggs had known about the old foundation before carrying out his dowsing survey.

Another church that Denis Briggs surveyed by dowsing was St. Nicholas's, Kyloe, spectacularly situated on the Northumberland coastline overlooking Holy Island. Although the first church on this site dated from the twelfth century, the existing church was built in the late-eighteenth century and enlarged in the nineteenth. Among the features that Denis Briggs predicted was a junction of two old foundations near the south wall of the nave and what seemed to be two old apses of different periods in the eastern part of the church. The archaeologists dug two separate trenches to test the dowser's predictions. The first showed no trace of the old foundation that Briggs had indicated on his plans. The second trench, however, produced exciting results. It revealed an old cobbled foundation in almost exactly the position predicted by the dowser.

Quite different in its setting from St. Nicholas's Kyloe, is the mediaeval church of St. John's in the city of Newcastle-upon-Tyne. Denis Briggs carried out a dowsing survey there in 1982 but it was not until February 1985 that the opportunity arose for the archaeologists to cut a small trench to test the accuracy of the dowser's plan. Denis Briggs had predicted that a linear feature would be found running in an easterly direction through the north aisle of the church. When the archaeologists dug their trench they found two brick structures close to the dowser's predicted line. Beneath these, and coinciding exactly in its dimensions with those predicted by Briggs was a slot in the underlying clay, which may have been an old foundation trench.

Denis Briggs surveyed another mediaeval church, St. Mary's Morpeth, in 1984. He predicted that a feature running in a north-north-east direction would be found beneath the eastern end of the nave. When Professor Bailey rapidly dug out a small trench in January 1985, he found an old mortared foundation coinciding exactly with the dowser's predictions. Bailey believed that the structure may have been the foundation of the eastern part of the nave before the rebuilding in the fourteenth century.

Altogether, the archaeologists carried out at least thirteen excavations to test the accuracy of Denis Briggs' dowsing. Of these, Professor Bailey would classify seven as successes and five as failures. This relatively high rate of success led Bailey to conclude that 'Archaeologists should now seriously consider adding dowsing to their battery of remote-sensing devices, on the simple grounds that it appears to work.'

Though some archaeologists disputed this conclusion, Bailey's judgement was echoed by a number of other British academics. On publication of a book detailing Denis Briggs' results[10] several distinguished academics including Philip Rahtz, emeritus professor of archaeology at the University of York and Dr Warwick Rodwell, a church archaeologist expressed enthusiasm for dowsing as an aid to archaeologists.[11]

5   The Sceptics Refuted

Our look at the long history of dowsing has shown that people like William Cookworthy, John Mullins, Charles Pogson and Hans Schröter have been amazingly successful in locating certain geological faults, fractures and fissures. Such fractures may be mineralized, water-bearing or may conduct the radioactive gas radon to the surface – sometimes with fatal consequences for people living above. Moreover, a few dowsers seem to have been able to pinpoint shallower underground features such as tunnels and archaeological remains.

How can we explain these dowsing achievements? For a start, we could ask the sceptics for their views. Here is one influential sceptic's comment on dowsing:

> It is difficult to see how for practical purposes the entire matter could have been more thoroughly discredited ... It is by no means true that all persons using a forked twig or some other device for locating water are intentional deceivers. Some of them are doubtless men of good character and benevolent intentions. However many of the large group of professionals are deliberately defrauding the people and the total amount of money they obtain is large.

These words were written in 1917 by O.E. Meinzer, of the US Geological Survey in his introduction to that organization's historical survey of dowsing.[1] But the hostile attitudes they represent are still held today – for instance by members of the Committee for the Scientific Investigation of Claims of the Paranormal (CSICOP) in the USA and its affiliates in other countries.[2, 3] Motivated by emotion rather than reason, such sceptics seek to deny the very phenomenon – successful dowsing – that we are trying to explain.

Clearly, debunkers of this persuasion will give us no help at all in explaining dowsing success. Fortunately there is a more constructive tradition of dowsing scepticism going back to the time of Robert Boyle. We may recall that while doubting that the rod was attracted to the mineral vein in the way that contemporary dowsers believed, Boyle nevertheless admitted that the technique seemed to work and believed the phenomenon should be investigated.

A more recent dowsing sceptic of this variety was the British psychologist D.H. Rawcliffe.[4] Acknowledging that some water dowsers, such as Major Pogson had outstandingly successful records, Rawcliffe believed that these could be explained without invoking any mysterious 'dowsing effect'. Rawcliffe argued that such dowsers unconsciously respond to a whole variety of subtle sensory cues. Some of them would be visual cues such as slight modifications in the colour of soil and vegetation, scarcely perceptible changes in the health and growth of plants, texture and dampness of the soil. Others could be tactile – for example the feel of the ground underfoot, while other senses such as smell and hearing might also be involved. But Rawcliffe admitted that his suggestions were speculative and further investigations were needed.

Several German Earth scientists have recently put forward similar ideas to explain the successes of Hans Schröter in Sri Lanka and elsewhere.[5, 6] They suggest that the engineer is a 'super-observer', who unconsciously notices very subtle changes in vegetation or other clues that might indicate the presence of water-bearing fissures below.

What distinguishes these constructive sceptics from the debunkers of the CSICOP school is that they acknowledge the facts of dowsing success, and propose testable theories, based on existing scientific knowledge, to account for them. They doubt only the need to seek new explanations for dowsing, not the actual achievements of dowsers as reported in this book. Accordingly, this group of sceptics do not, as the debunkers do, regard dowsing as invalid. They merely point out that as (in their view) dowsers receive all their information by means of conventional senses, the technique has a limited value, affords no new scientific insights, and offers little potential for further development.

But how can such sceptics be sure in advance that known scientific theory can explain all dowsing success? Of course, they can't, all they can do is tell us to be sensible and look first at accepted theory, testing its ability to explain dowsers' successes by means of appropriate experiments. As Sir Karl Popper, the philosopher, has shown,[7] such experiments should be designed to expose the weaknesses of existing theory, not confirm its strong points. If none of the experimental results contradict the sceptics' theory, then we may regard it as the best available. If, on the other hand, the results of crucial experiments do not accord with the sceptics' theory of successful dowsing, we will have to abandon it or at least modify it in some way.

Armed with these ideas, we can now try to evaluate the numerous controlled dowsing experiments that scientists have carried out over the years. In each case we should ask the following questions: Did the researchers test the strongest dowsing claim – that of outstanding dowsers to detect mineralized or water-bearing fissures and faults? Do the results actually support the sceptics' theory – that dowsers achieve above-chance results by responding to visual or other conventional sensory cues – or do they refute it? Although this last question seems too obvious to need stating, several investigators have been so prejudiced – for or against dowsing – that they have played down any results that did not confirm their own preconceived beliefs. We should therefore always look at the results themselves, not just the investigator's conclusions.

Bearing these criteria in mind, what can we learn from the dowsing experiments that psychologists and others have carried out in the past? Some early tests were certainly instructive. For instance, in the 1920s, a Minnesota pastor claimed that by using a forked twig he could determine the depth at which a box of metal objects was located.[8] Some psychologists at the University of Minnesota devised an experiment to test the man's claim. They placed the box on different steps of a ladder which was one floor below the pastor and hidden from his view. But they also placed six spectators on a landing in such a way that they could see the pastor on the floor above as well as the box on the floor below.

When tested, the dowser scored much better than chance in determining correctly upon which step of the concealed ladder the investigators had placed the box. Yet in achieving this result he had demonstrated no magical powers. When the box was placed on a high step, the spectators had to stoop to see it. When it was placed on a lower step, no stooping was required. The pastor had – perhaps unconsciously – observed the behaviour of the spectators and thereby gained enough information to score well.

In this experiment, the sceptics' theory accounts well for the pastor's success. The results show that dowsers indeed respond to visual cues, including hints provided by those recording the dowsers' results. They suggest that all dowsing tests should ideally be carried out in double-blind mode, in which neither the dowser nor those conducting the experiments know the correct results of the tests.

The experiment with the Minnesota pastor nevertheless failed hopelessly as a general test of the sceptics' theory because the claim examined was one of the weakest it is possible to imagine.

Divination of the depth of a hidden object has nothing to do with traditional dowsing.

Investigators have tested very weak dowsing claims of this kind on numerous occasions, confirming beyond doubt that the sceptics' theory holds good in such cases. For instance, the University of Minnesota psychologists mentioned above carried out other tests with their dowsing clergyman.[9] The pastor claimed that with his forked twig he could find water, metals and so on. But instead of testing his ability to detect mineralized or water-bearing fissures in the field, the psychologists took him into their laboratory and found that he could not locate samples of metals or water hidden in the building. As we have seen, there is no historical evidence that dowsers can detect such samples – the dowsing claim tested was a very weak one indeed.

In their influential study of dowsing, *Water Witching USA*, Evon Vogt and Ray Hyman make much of another such experiment, carried out in the late 1940s.[10] A group of psychologists wanted to test the effectiveness of water dowsing. However, instead of investigating the traditional claim of dowsers to find water-filled fissures, the psychologists tested twenty-seven dowsers at a field in Maine where water was present everywhere a few feet below the surface. The psychologists asked each dowser to find the best site for a well. When holes were subsequently drilled on the dowsers' chosen sites, all were, naturally enough, successful.

But instead of admitting that all the dowsers had succeeded in finding water, the psychologists assessed them solely on their claims to forecast water depth and yield, comparing their predictions with similar forecasts made by a geologist and a water engineer. Not surprisingly, the dowsers' predictions turned out to be less accurate than those made by the two experts.

One interesting result did emerge from this experiment. Ten of the sites chosen by the dowsers (who had in some cases been blindfolded) lay very close to a straight line. This would have suggested to anyone familiar with the history of dowsing that the dowsers may indeed have been responding to a linear underground feature. But the investigating psychologists ignored this intriguing aspect of their results. They concluded that their experiments had shown no evidence in favour of dowsing.

Even when investigators have tested somewhat stronger dowsing claims, the significance of the results has not always been clear. Thus in 1971 the engineer R.A. Foulkes, of the Institute for Industrial Research and Standards, Dublin, carried out a number of tests on behalf of the British Ministry of

Defence. These included a series of experiments to see whether or not dowsers could detect and distinguish between mines and other buried objects. The claims tested were thus still relatively weak ones, as our historical survey has shown no evidence that dowsers can distinguish between different buried objects. However, as the buried metal mines might be expected to share some features with dowsers' traditional targets, the tests were at least slightly more realistic than the ones we have just looked at.

Foulkes arranged for the objects – metal mines, plastic mines, and concrete and wooden dummy mines – to be buried at random in a grid pattern. Half of the test site consisted of heather-clad heathland while the other half was cleared of vegetation and raked level. The dowsers were asked to walk over each grid square and to say whether or not a buried object was present and if so whether it was a metal mine or a plastic one. The dowsers were not told about the other buried objects.

Despite the difficulty of Foulkes' tests, some of the dowsers actually performed very well indeed. In their recent report for the German government – discussed later in the chapter – Professor Hans Betz, a physicist at the University of Munich and Professor Herbert König, a physicist at the Technical University of Munich, have shown that two out of the twelve dowsers who completed all Foulkes' tests each got results that would only occur by chance on less than two occasions out of ten thousand.[11] Taking into account the good performance of a third dowser, the odds were less than one-in-a-thousand that the overall outcome of these mine detection tests resulted from chance.

In his own report, however, Foulkes conspicuously failed to acknowledge the dowsers' success, concluding that, 'There is no real evidence of any dowsing ability which could produce results better than chance or guessing.'[12] This biased conclusion was a classic example of an orthodox scientist impatient to demonstrate that dowsing is nonsense. Had Foulkes given more thought to the question, he would have realized that his dowsers' above-chance results might still be consistent with the sceptics' theory of dowsing success. Both the natural heathland and the raked soil could have provided subtle visual indications that mines were buried below, and these could have enabled the skilled dowsers to come up with above-chance scores. But, as a debunker, Foulkes could not bring himself to admit *any* dowsing success, even when predicted by the sceptics' own theory.

Attempts were made to resolve this question of visual cues in another series of dowsing experiments carried out in England in the same year. By this time, many engineers with the various regional Electricity Boards in Britain were using dowsing to help locate the positions of underground cables, pipes and drains. Robert McAnulla, a member of staff at the Electricity Research Council's Research Centre at Capenhurst, decided to test these dowsers' claims.[13, 14] Although relatively weak, the claims were still worth looking at as buried cables, pipes and the like might still have something in common with dowsers' traditional geological targets.

Eight dowsers walked along a series of test paths in the grounds of the Capenhurst Research Centre. An observer, who did not know the positions of underground cables, water mains, sewers and drains, recorded the places where the dowsers' rods moved. The results showed that the dowsers performed significantly better than chance in locating the buried utilities. McAnulla concluded that 'certain people have the ability to locate underground objects using dowsing rods'.

But could the dowsers have unconsciously observed tell-tale signs that helped them get their good results? To test this idea, four members of the technical staff at Capenhurst walked along the same test paths as the dowsers, with instructions to look around carefully and then estimate the locations of the cables and other features. When this was done, it turned out that the technical staff had performed better than the dowsers.

Despite McAnulla's pro-dowsing conclusions, the results of the Electricity Council's experiments therefore undeniably agreed with the sceptics' predictions – a mirror image of the way the Ministry of Defence's results were presented. But for sceptics to congratulate themselves at that stage would have been premature, for they had not yet shown that their theory could explain the strongest dowsing claims.

Further experiments were clearly needed and this challenge was taken up by Duane Chadwick, a professor in the College of Engineering at the Logan campus of Utah State University in the USA. In the arid Mormon State of Utah, water dowsers had plied their craft for generations and stories of their successes were commonplace. Chadwick had heard the dowsers' tales but remained sceptical – he knew how easy it was for dowsers to fool themselves.

Chadwick felt, however, that dowsing should not be dismissed without investigation, and it was in this spirit of scientific curiosity that he devised his dowsing experiments.[15] He reasoned that if dowsers really could detect underground features, then, even in the absence of sensory cues, their rods should move in the same places. On the other hand, if the sceptics' theory was true, their rods should move randomly.

To test this concept, he organized tests involving more than 150 people – mainly students and staff at Utah State University –

at four locations, three in Logan, Utah and one in Lorton, Virginia. At each location, the dowsers walked with L-shaped rods along a series of natural test paths, dropping small wooden blocks at the places where their rods moved. They also participated in control experiments which involved 'dowsing without rods' – in other words dropping blocks where they felt like doing so.

The results of the tests surprised Chadwick. Instead of being randomly distributed, as the sceptics' theory predicted, the dowsers' rod movements showed very high degrees of clustering at the three Logan sites and some clustering at the Virginian site. In all cases, the dowsers' responses clustered together far more than did the blocks in the control experiments.

Although Chadwick tested novice dowsers rather than experienced ones and it was not clear what, if anything, they were detecting, the strong tendency of dowsers to move their rods in the same places, even in the absence of obvious visual cues, did cast doubt on the sceptics' theory. Chadwick's personal scepticism was certainly shaken, and he concluded that further investigations were needed. However Chadwick's findings were largely ignored by orthodox scientists.

Because of the lack of publicity given to these findings, during the 1970s and early 1980s most scientists continued to ignore the subject completely. True enough, in 1982 the Geographical Institute at the University of Lund in Sweden carried out an investigation that showed excellent correlations between dowsing responses and geophysical anomalies.[16] In 1986 the Technical University at Graz in Austria conducted experiments with water dowsers that yielded highly significant results.[17] But it was not until 1987 that Duane Chadwick's call for further dowsing research was taken up seriously when a team of German scientists, funded by the Federal Government, began the most comprehensive investigation of dowsing ever undertaken.[18]

Credit for mounting the study should go not so much to the scientific community itself though but to the former West German President, Professor Dr Karl Carstens and his wife, Dr Veronica Carstens. The presidential couple's endorsement of the subject reflected a longstanding German popular interest in the possibility – discussed in chapter three – that dowsers can detect 'harmful Earth rays'. President Carstens and his wife hoped that a major investigation of dowsing might shed light on this vitally important question. In 1981 they set up a foundation for the study of the 'Earth ray' puzzle, dowsing and other allied problems.

President Carstens' personal initiative coincided in its

objectives with those of an ongoing German government programme to carry out research into unconventional ways of fighting cancer. These two government efforts prompted a number of German scientists, who had long felt uneasy at orthodox science's dismissive attitude to dowsing, to openly declare their support for a new, high-quality, investigation of the subject.

As a first step in the implementation of their programme, the interested parties invited twenty-four distinguished scientists to a meeting at the Schloss Reisensburg Castle in January 1984. The participants included Dr Veronica Carstens, the Munich physicists Professors Hans Betz and Herbert König – who would later act as joint executive leaders of the project – and Professor Herbert Fröhlich, FRS, a physicist from the University of Liverpool who had pioneered the application of many principles of electromagnetism to biological systems. At the meeting the experts agreed that the priority was to find out whether or not a dowsing effect really existed – in other words to comprehensively test the sceptics' theory of dowsing success.

When the project got fully under way in 1987 the scientists first conducted a pilot study which included tests similar to those carried out by Duane Chadwick at Utah State University. Dowsers – 61 in the first test and 244 in the second – walked over two different level test paths. They used a weird variety of rods, not only classical horizontally held V-rods made of plastic or steel wire, but also vertical rods similar to those used by the Soviet geologist-dowsers, described in chapter one. The investigators, who, like the dowsers had no previous knowledge of the test courses, carefully noted the places where the dowsers' rods moved. When the results were plotted, they showed the same striking patterns that Duane Chadwick had found in his experiments. The dowsers' rod movements showed highly significant degrees of clustering – as would be expected if the dowsers really were detecting underground features.

However, sceptics could point out that the dowsers could merely have been responding to the same visual cues – even a conspicuous tuft of grass might be enough to trigger a dowsing response. The German scientists could see that the only way to find out once and for all whether the sceptics' theory was true or false would be to screen the dowsers, as they walked along, from all normal sensory information.

One way of achieving this would be to find out if dowsers, screened in this way, could detect artificial dowsing targets. But instead of using simple samples of metals and water as the University of Minnesota psychologists had done many years before, they tried to create targets more closely resembling the actual field situation where water flows through a narrow fissure. The German scientists constructed a variety of artificial targets by passing water through copper or plastic pipes or through an artificial pebble bed.

The scientists carried out this series of experiments in a two-storey barn, north of the city of Munich, that seemed ideal for their purposes. They placed the artificial dowsing targets on the ground floor of the building. The actual position of the target in successive tests was selected at random by a computer.

By mounting steps outside the barn the dowsers climbed directly to the floor above the one containing the target objects. Sound insulation prevented the dowsers from receiving any audible cues concerning the position of the target. On the upper floor, an experimental assistant with no knowledge of the target's position, noted the locations of the dowser's responses as he walked along. The experiments were therefore carried out under full double-blind conditions.

In all, forty-three dowsers, including Hans Schröter, took part in a total of about 900 single tests. Although the majority performed little or no better than chance, a few experienced dowsers performed very well, while Hans Schröter turned in the best performance of all. In one series of tests to see if he could detect water flowing through a copper pipe, Schröter came up with results that could only have been duplicated by chance on less than one in five hundred occasions. Altogether the odds were less than seven in a thousand that the results of all forty-three dowsers could have occurred by chance.

While the ability of Hans Schröter and a few other seasoned dowsers to locate artificial dowsing targets in controlled laboratory conditions seemed to refute the sceptics' theory of dowsing success, the overall results of the barn experiments did not provide spectacular evidence in favour of a dowsing effect. The investigators decided to try to obtain more decisive results by testing dowsers in the field rather than in a laboratory environment.

With this in mind, the Munich group of scientists developed two special dowsing test devices. The first was a long wagon, enclosed to screen off visual cues, which could be towed to various sites of interest. The wagon consisted of a 10 metre-long wooden platform, mounted on eight small wheels and supporting a fabric-covered wooden frame. After positioning the wagon at a site of interest, the investigators took the blindfolded dowser to the test site by car. They then transferred the still blindfolded subject into the wagon. Once inside, blindfolds were removed and the dowser walked along the length of the wagon. An experimental assistant inside the wagon then noted the places where the dowser's rod moved.

Despite the wagon's ingenious construction, the scientists found that in practice it was very difficult and time-consuming to manoeuvre it into the correct position at suitable test sites. Clearly an alternative had to be found. The device the scientists came up with was similar in principle to the wagon but much simpler – a very long wooden plank. Actually the device consisted of three separate planks, joined together side by side and resting on a level base. While the central plank was horizontal, the two on either side were tilted inwards so as to guide the footsteps of the dowser – who remained blindfolded during the tests – straight along the middle of the plank. To prevent dowsers from getting information from any irregularities on the surface of the plank as they walked along, the wooden surface was completely smooth or carpeted.

Once the investigators had positioned the plank at the site of interest, an experimental assistant disorientated each dowser before he or she started to walk. A second assistant noted the precise positions where the dowser's rod moved. The test would then be repeated a number of times.

Critics could raise an obvious objection to the procedure just described: even if the dowsers did not know exactly where they were, by counting their paces, they could always determine how far they had walked along the plank from their starting position. By moving their rods after walking the same distances in successive tests, the dowsers could appear to be consistently detecting underground features, though in fact they were responding only to the information in their own brains. To meet this objection, each dowser began successive walks from random computer-selected starting positions on the first half of the plank.

Critics could still object that although the scientists seemed to have honed their experimental protocol until it was free from flaws, the statistical processing of the results might remain open to question. The investigators might select only the better results for processing, thereby falsifying the overall outcome of the experiments. To obviate this possibility, all experimental data was processed independently by the highly respected Institute for Medical Information and Systems Research in Munich.

When the statistical analyses of the first plank experiments came in, the results seemed to support the sceptics' explanation of dowsing success. Again and again, the dowsers' turned in near-chance results.

At this stage, it seemed likely that the German dowsing tests would end on this note. Although the above-chance ability of

Hans Schröter and a few other experienced dowsers to locate artificial dowsing targets in controlled experiments had cast doubt on the sceptics' explanation of dowsing success, the results were not impressive enough to be conclusive. The dowsers' failure to achieve significant results in the more realistic plank tests would bring smiles of smug self-satisfaction to the sceptics' faces. The dowsers would retreat to their ghetto of irrationalism and science would continue to regard their art as nothing more than a time-wasting nuisance.

Such was the situation in the spring of 1988. But in the summer of that year, a remarkable development took place. The scientists discovered a site where the dowsers could get highly significant, repeatable results.

The discovery was the result of an actual field dowsing operation.[19] A German mineral water company had for many years extracted naturally carbonated water from deep boreholes in the Sinn valley, north of the town of Rieneck in north-west Bavaria. The area had been well explored, not only for carbon dioxide and mineral water but also for uranium ore, and several deep boreholes had been drilled. As a result the general features of the local geology were well known. Beneath the valley alluvium lay a thick sequence of sedimentary rocks consisting of Zechstein Limestone overlain by several hundred metres of Bunter Sandstone. A major north-west-running fault ran along the valley floor beneath the alluvium, while a number of shorter north-east-trending fractures cut across the major fault. The precise positions of these faults were, however, somewhat uncertain.

The mineral water company now desperately needed a new source of carbonated water, having over the years drilled several holes without success. Because of the great depth – about 400 metres – of the fracture systems considered likely to hold carbonated water, conventional geophysical methods were not considered feasible and the company therefore decided to try dowsing.

The first dowser the company employed selected a site in a meadow on the valley alluvium, just north of a bend in the River Sinn. Later, when the Munich group were investigating the abilities of Hans Schröter and other dowsers, it was arranged that Schröter himself would undertake a dowsing survey for the company.

In June 1988, Hans Schröter carried out his dowsing survey, indicating the exact positions of suspected faults as well as his preferred borehole site. He located this directly over a point where he suspected one of the cross-cutting fractures intersected with the major valley fault. Whether this was a

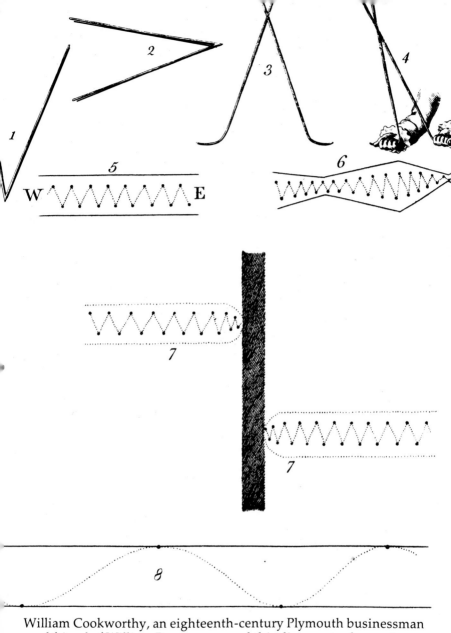

William Cookworthy, an eighteenth-century Plymouth businessman and friend of William Pryce composed this diagram to show miners how to trace hidden lodes of metal ore. Cut a suitable forked twig from a tree (1,2) or tie two straight shoots together (3). Firmly hold the rod in a 'palms up' position (4). To trace the margins of a wide lode (5,8), start in the middle at W and walk outwards until the rod flips, indicating the outer margin of the lode. Then turn round and locate the opposite margin in a similar fashion. Continue to trace the margins of the lode, walking in a zigzag manner, until you reach E. You can trace irregular lodes (6), or those displaced by cross-cutting fractures (7) in exactly the same way

2ᵉ Manier de tenir la Baguette.

Jacques Aymar is pictured responding to 'corpuscles' rising from a mineral vein or underground water source (1693)

A dowser holds his rod in an unusual manner, balancing his rod on the back of his outstretched hand (1693)

Professor Yves Rocard attempting to stimulate the minute magnetite crystals he believed were in the human head

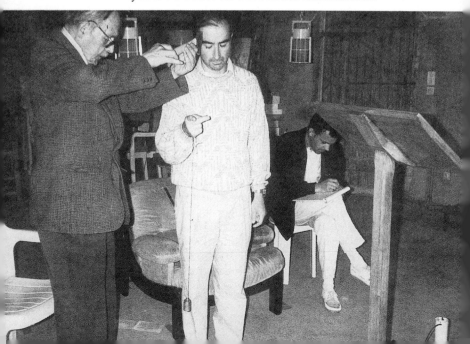

sensible site for a very deep vertical borehole is open to question, bearing in mind that the inclined fault planes would diverge away from the borehole with increasing depth. Nevertheless, that is where Schröter sited it, and remarkably, it was only about 10 metres away from the first dowser's site.

Requiring a third opinion, the company now called in Andrei Apostol, the Romanian-born dowser and geophysicist mentioned in chapter one, by then based in New York. Having had much experience of dowsing both for faults and sources of carbon dioxide, Apostol was well qualified for the job. Apostol flew in from New York in July and conducted a dowsing survey of the area, indicating the dowsed positions of the faults.

When the investigators compared Apostol's dowsing results with those of Schröter, they found the agreement remarkable. Apostol's dowsing had also indicated that a cross-cutting fracture intersected the main valley fault, the intersection lying only about 10 metres from Schröter's preferred borehole site.

The results so far, although interesting, could still be explained by the sceptics' theory of dowsing success. Hans Schröter and Andrei Apostol may have suspected beforehand that the faults existed, and by carefully observing topographic clues they might have reached similar conclusions. Indeed, Andrei has admitted to me that bends in the River Sinn and other clues could have helped Schröter and himself locate the faults.[20] It was not until the Munich group of scientists carried out a series of plank experiments with blindfolded dowsers at Hans Schröter's borehole site that really surprising results started to emerge.

The investigators positioned the long wooden plank right on top of Schröter's site. Then, when weather conditions were suitable, the scientists tested the blindfolded dowsers in the normal way, following the meticulous protocols that they had developed and refined in the previous year.

When the data had been processed, the results turned out to be quite remarkable. Of the first four dowsers tested, two had succeeded in locating Hans Schröter's site with an uncanny precision. Despite complete disorientation and random starting positions, on each successive walk the rods of the two blindfolded dowsers had moved within one metre or so of the point that Hans Schröter had selected. In each case, the odds that the dowser's results could have occurred by chance were less than one thousand to one. The third dowser also produced above-chance results: his rod movements clustered just beyond Hans Schröter's well site.

As the experiments continued, novice dowsers as well as seasoned water finders succeeded in locating the borehole site.

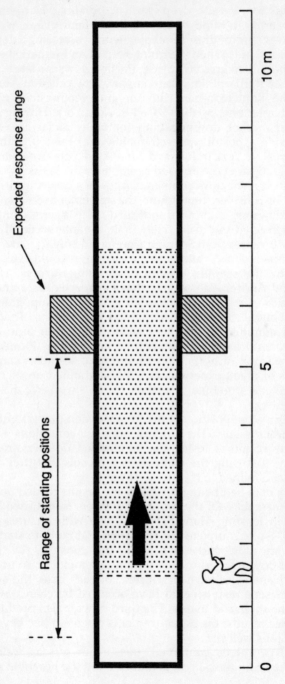

Fig.2 Principle of the plank experiments devised to test dowsers' claims by the government-funded Munich group of scientists. Blindfolded, disorientated dowsers walked along a specially designed wooden plank placed over a site of interest. Dowsers walked a fixed distance, each time starting at a different point selected randomly by computer. An observer recorded the places where the dowsers' rods moved

How the Munich group's plank experiments refuted the sceptics' explanation of successful dowsing

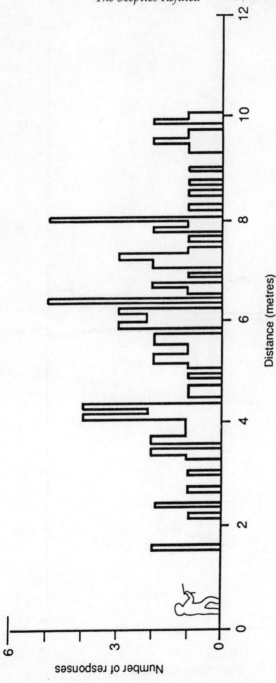

Fig.3a In many series of plank experiments, blindfolded dowsers moved their rods randomly, as the sceptics' theory predicted. This diagram shows the cumulative responses of one dowser who walked along the plank forty times, starting at a different point each time

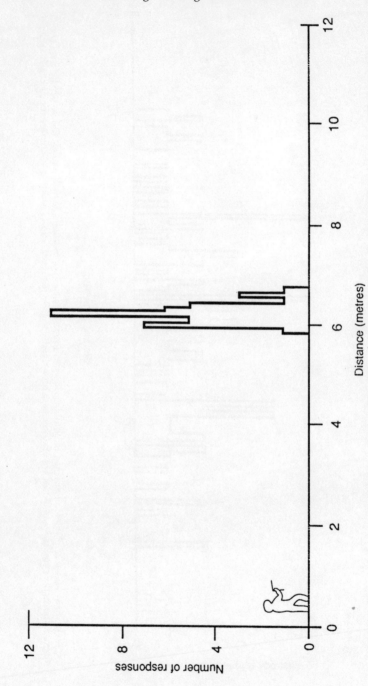

Fig.3b When the investigators placed the plank over a borehole site chosen by Hans Schröter, above a concealed geological fault, very different results emerged. The diagram again shows the cumulative responses of a dowser who walked along the plank forty times, starting at a different point each time. But this time the dowser always responded within a metre of Hans Schröter's site. Other ... ability to locate the hidden fault under controlled experimental conditions

When the investigators put together all the results of the forty dowsers who had taken part in the plank experiments, at this site and elsewhere, they found that thirteen had produced significant results, of whom nine had performed at a highly significant level. Seven of the dowsers had come up with consistently good results in repeated experiments. *The odds were less than one in a million that all the results of the forty dowsers' could be explained by chance.*

One question remained, though. Could the scientists be sure that Hans Schröter's borehole site really did lie directly above a geological fault? To resolve this issue, the investigators conducted electrical resistivity surveys in the area around the borehole site. The results suggested that the suspected fault indeed lay directly beneath the dowser's site.[21]

It is impossible to exaggerate the significance of these results. The sceptics' theory of dowsing worked only when tested on weak dowsing claims. When invoked to explain the results of a realistic dowsing experiment – experienced dowsers searching for a concealed geological fault – it failed. It is a failure that opens the way to a new search for the dowsers' secret of success.

6   The Riddle of the Sphinx

The sceptics' inability to explain how, in controlled experiments, blindfolded dowsers could detect a hidden geological fault means that we must look afresh at dowsing theory. But before we can hope to understand how some dowsers have achieved success, we need to look again at the old question: what causes dowsers' rods to flip? Thanks to the observations of Agricola, Kircher, de Vallemont and others, we know that dowsers themselves move their rods, but what actually causes their arm muscles to contract, forcing the delicately balanced rod to twist?

Some people have argued that when dowsers walk over geological faults or other underground features, they experience physiological changes which cause the muscle contractions to take place. A leading advocate of this view was Dr Solco Tromp, the Dutch geologist and dowsing investigator already mentioned in chapter two. After spending a period as Professor of Geology at Fuad I University in Egypt, Tromp returned to the Netherlands in the late 1940s and devoted the latter part of his scientific career to the emerging science of biometeorology. In his many scholarly publications Tromp cited numerous experiments showing how small meteorological and geophysical changes could affect human beings and their health. Tromp believed that dowsing fitted into this spectrum: in his view, when a dowser walks over a hidden geological discontinuity, he or she experiences an automatic, robot-like response – termed a muscle tone reflex – that causes the rod to flip.[1, 2, 3, 4]

In principle, Tromp's idea is a sound one. Mineral veins and faults produce geophysical perturbations that could conceivably act directly on the dowser's body in the manner Tromp envisaged. Dowsing lore is replete with tales of dowsers reacting to underground water in the most violent manner. We may recall how, as a youngster, Barthelemy Bléton was allegedly seized with a fever whenever he sat down to rest at a particular place. Later, so the story goes, a spring of water was found beneath that very spot.

But this view of the dowsing 'reflex' as a physiological response to a geophysical perturbation has a fundamental weakness. It cannot explain why dowsers also move their rods in response to visual hints or other sensory cues. As the sceptics have pointed out, there is a lot of evidence that dowsers unconsciously use any available cues that may help them locate their underground targets. Yet, when using such cues, their rods continue to flip in the normal fashion.

In order to square their theory with the evidence, followers of Tromp have to divide dowsers' rod movements into two separate categories: a tiny minority of true, physiological dowsing reactions and a vast majority of false, psychological responses. But since even dowsers themselves cannot distinguish the true reactions from the false ones, we may well feel that this distinction smacks more of religious faith than objective science. It seems far more likely that all dowsing reactions are of the same kind and are initiated by the brain rather than the body.

Those two prominent sceptics, Evon Vogt and Ray Hyman, give a good account of how this seems to happen.[5] They ask us to picture a potential dowser, Jim Brooks, watching an experienced 'water witch' or diviner dowse a well for a local farmer, Frank Brown:

> The diviner grasps the forked twig in the standard grip, forearms tense, head and body leaning forward, eyes fixed upon the butt end of the rod, and proceeds to walk carefully about Frank Brown's property.
>
> Jim watches the trancelike absorption of the diviner with interest. From what we know about implicit muscular responses, we can assume that microscopic muscular contractions are taking place in Jim's forearms as he intently follows the behaviour of the diviner. Perhaps Jim's neck muscles and general musculature are tense as he leans forward awaiting the outcome of the diviner's quest for water. Already the idea has been implanted, and implicit muscular responses have occurred. Suddenly the divining rod dramatically springs forward and points down. The diviner stops and looks up as if suddenly awakened from a trance.
>
> The diviner notices Jim Brooks' incredulous gaze. He walks up to Jim and hands him the rod, telling him it will also work for him. As a result of this direct suggestion, Jim's forearm muscles again make microscopic contractions as the idea of duplicating the diviner's performance leads to this imperceptible acting-out …
>
> Jim grasps the rod in the same grip that he saw the diviner use. His arms tense, his eyes fixed upon the rod's point, he becomes oblivious of the surrounding spectators as he concentrates upon the dominant theme of the rod's actions. The increased tension in his arms and body facilitates muscular response. An impulse that might not lead to overt muscular action in a relaxed muscle may

be sufficient to trigger off such action in a tense one. This heightened and prolonged tension, furthermore, masks the neural feedback from his arms and hands. The focusing of his attention on the dominant idea further enhances the effectiveness of the expectation that the rod will move.

Now Jim is nearing the site over which the diviner's rod had dipped. The image of the rod's movements becomes much stronger in the face of the expectancy that it will move. The contractions in the forearm spread to adjoining fibres; the minute contractions begin rallying together. Suddenly the minute contractions – in a great wave of unison – produce a larger muscular contraction. With an almost imperceptible spasm the hands suddenly come closer together and the wrists turn slightly inward. This action upsets the delicate balance of forces existing between Jim's grip and the tensions in the rod. The rod suddenly springs forward with such force that the bark peels off and Jim's hands become painfully scratched. Jim suddenly is aware that the rod has dipped – seemingly of its own accord – over the same spot as it had for the diviner. At first he is at a loss for words. Then he is overcome with a desire to explain to the onlookers that he did not make the rod move; indeed he was conscious only of an attempt to hold back the rod. He points to the peeled bark and his injured hands as proof. Perhaps the onlookers will believe him; perhaps some will scoff. But Jim has now entered the ranks of the water diviners.

Anyone familiar with dowsing will recognize how convincingly Vogt and Hyman portray a novice's first dowsing experience. The initial impulse for the dowsing response clearly comes from the mind rather than the body. But because the impulse comes from the unconscious part of the mind, dowsers like Jim are unaware of any intention to move the rod and its sudden movement takes them by surprise. This experience can be so powerful as to turn even a confirmed sceptic into a life-long believer in dowsing.

Moreover, the two authors' emphasis of the rôle of suggestion in dowsing explains why some dowsers are so ready to confirm each other's claims, however ludicrous they may be. As we saw in chapter three, no sooner had Baron von Pohl found electric currents flowing under the beds of sick people than other dowsers also found such currents. The practice grew explosively and today the Baron's crazy cult has a huge following.

But why do dowsers flip their rods in particular places? Vogt and Hyman point out that in the trance-like dowsing state, dowsers are unusually receptive to sensory cues – the slightest visual or other hint may be enough to trigger a dowsing response. In the case of Baron von Pohl and his followers, visual cues – such as the sight of patients' beds – would always have been available as these medical dowsers walked around their patients' rooms. The constant availability of appropriate visual cues neatly explains why members of the Baron's bed-moving cult *always* find electric currents, Earth rays or whatever in association with their patients' beds.

All this suggests that the sceptics' proposed mechanism for the dowser's response is basically correct. But how then did the dowsers tested by the Munich group of scientists locate a hidden geological fault in the absence of conventional sensory cues? To answer this crucial question, we need to look more closely at the source of the dowser's impulse to move his or her rods – the unconscious mind. As Vogt and Hyman put it 'The unconscious muscular reaction results from a suggestion from the subconsciousness of the diviner.'

Any mention of the subconscious is liable to bring to mind the name of Sigmund Freud whose speculations have exerted such a potent influence on twentieth-century thought. Do the Freudians have an explanation of the dowsers' response? Indeed they do, and it is not difficult to guess how it goes. The psychoanalysts interpret the dowser's response as the symbolic acting out of his subconscious wish to have sexual intercourse with his mother in order to return to the womb. The rod, of course, represents the penis while the ground below – Mother Earth – is the mother.[6]

It seems unlikely that anyone acquainted with dowsing has taken the Freudian theory of dowsing seriously and in any case this rather unimaginative idea cannot explain how a dowser's subconscious mind can locate a hidden geological fault. But if the Freudians' writings are of little use to us when they tackle the subject of dowsing directly, we can at least find some indirect pointers towards the solution of our puzzle in the musings of the most famous of all Freud's pupils, Carl Gustav Jung.

The sage of Zürich devoted much time to the interpretation of dreams, being particularly interested in certain recurrent dream images which he thought were timeless symbols of universal significance for humanity. Amongst these were various gods, goddesses and mythological beings such as centaurs, satyrs, the Chimaera and the Sphinx. Of all these beings, the one that can perhaps help us most in our quest for the source of the dowser's mysterious subconscious powers is that most enigmatic of creatures, the Sphinx.

When we think of these human-headed lions, the image that first springs to mind is the colossal Sphinx at Giza in Egypt, who has gazed inscrutably across the Western Desert for more than 4,000 years. But the Egyptian Sphinx was only the oldest member of a family that included the winged sphinxes of Asia and Greece. The Greek Sphinx of classical mythology, the 'dark prophetess' of Ovid, was a winged goddess, with the head of a lovely woman, the body of a lioness, the wings of an eagle and the tail of a serpent. She had some dreadful relatives: her mother, Echidne, a daughter of Gaia or Mother Earth, was half woman half serpent and ate men raw. One of the Sphinx's brothers was Cerberus, the three-headed Hound of Hell, another was the Chimaera, a fire-breathing goat with a lion's head and serpent's body. As if this were not bad enough, a third brother, the two-headed hound Orthrus, was also her father.

But in Jung's view, the Sphinx was not just a mythical monster with some rather unpleasant relatives. He saw her as a powerful archetype symbolically linking two dichotomies: human with animal and conscious with unconscious.[7] We may think we are purely human, but the Sphinx reminds us that on an unconscious level we are not only driven by animal instincts but may possess unsuspected animal-like powers. Could these mysterious powers help us solve the riddle of how a blindfolded dowser can detect a hidden geological fault?

7   When the Snakes Awake

The Sphinx had the tail of a serpent. To begin our enquiry into the possible animal-like powers of the dowser's unconscious mind, we might therefore start by looking at the sensory abilities of these slithery reptiles. For instance, certain snakes can detect their prey in total darkness. Could the possession of this reptilian supersense help a blindfolded dowser detect a hidden geological fault?

The snakes' secret, it turns out, lies in a thermal imaging capability rivalling the most advanced systems used by the armed forces of today.[1] Rattlesnakes and other pit vipers have pit organs beneath their eyes that focus heat waves – chiefly in the far infra-red band of the electromagnetic spectrum – to form a crude image. The heat image falls on a grid consisting of thousands of nerve endings. The nerves pass the information to the snake's brain for processing, and, if necessary, the initiation of appropriate action.

The organs are so sensitive that the animals can detect changes in temperature as small as 0.003 degrees centigrade. The snakes can therefore locate and devour tasty warm-blooded rodents under almost any conditions.

Can human beings, too, detect heat waves? While we cannot focus thermal infra-red waves to form images in the way that rattlesnakes do, we can detect the heat produced when, like ocean rollers, the waves break against our skins and dissipate their energy. Nerve endings in the skin a millimetre or so apart respond to temperature changes and send the information to the brain. Our conscious perception of the thermal infra-red waves is therefore crude.

However, our unconscious sensitivity seems to be much greater – to the extent that we can actually 'see' different colours with our hands. In his extraordinary book *The Black Goddess and the Sixth Sense* the scientifically trained British poet Peter Redgrove tells us how to carry out an experiment to demonstrate this:

> Cut out identical squares of variously coloured paper, and get somebody else to lay them on a table so you do not know the

positions, of the coloured squares. Now devise a blindfold you can't peer down, which is difficult, or, better, use some sort of covering over the table, under which you can slip your hands. Now, *feel with your hands for the colour of the paper.* Call out the colour you feel, and see whether the square you pull out is this colour.

You will not be right every time and some people are much better at this than others. You have to learn the feeling in the hands that changes as you pass them over the squares. Some people eventually get it right every time. It is best to begin by rubbing the hands briskly together, as a masseur will.[2]

What is the explanation for this remarkable unconscious ability? It seems that the skin of our hands acts rather like a radar scanner, though bouncing waves of infra-red rather than radio wavelengths off the coloured targets. The different coloured squares of paper reflect slightly different amounts of infra-red radiation back to our hands. But although the nerve endings in our skin can just detect these tiny differences and send the data to the brain, the information is not presented to our consciousness. It is only when we are forced to *guess* the correct colour that the hidden supersensory information comes to light.

These ideas have profound implications for dowsing. For when a dowser walks along searching for an underground target, he or she is in effect guessing its actual position in just the same way. The guessing process itself might therefore allow the dowser access to his or her hidden, supersensory powers.

Could, then, an unconscious snake-like sensitivity to infra-red heat rays play a part in successful dowsing? From the seventeenth century onwards, certain dowsers have had an excellent track record in finding thermal springs and it is quite possible that these successes owe something to an unwitting use of this supersense.

There are also wider possibilities. Concealed faults, mineral veins and water-bearing fissures may give rise to minute temperature changes in the ground immediately above. Dowsers who have learned how to access their thermal supersense might thereby detect such underground structures.[3] So already we have found an idea well worth investigating.

What other unconscious supersenses could a dowser use in this way? If we bear in mind the leonine body of the Sphinx, we immediately think of smell, for like so many other mammals, these large cats employ this sense far more widely than we do. This remarkable ability to detect chemical molecules in the air helps animals locate their food, avoid predators, find their way around and indulge in many other activities. A sense of smell is likely to have originated with almost the first living things and is perhaps the most universal of all animal senses.

In higher vertebrates, including ourselves, molecules of odorous substances in the air are wafted to the mucus-covered tissue in our noses as we breathe. Olfactory receptors – modified nerve cells – convert the smelly information into nerve impulses, which travel to the olfactory regions of the cortex in the same way that those from the retina pass to the visual cortex. The smell picture presented to human consciousness, though much simpler than the visual computer display that we see, is equally indescribable in words. It is interesting to reflect on the fact that the nerve signal data which give rise to our conscious experiences of vision and smell are of exactly the same kind; if the nerves were connected up the other way round we would smell different colours and see different smells.

Though less complex than the detailed kaleidoscope of vision, smells have the power to bring pleasure or distaste, convey deep emotional feelings and can even reawaken long-forgotten memories in a way that sights cannot. This instant capacity of smells to deliver powerful non-verbal messages gives us an insight into the far richer olfactory world that animals inhabit. If the smell of food is appetizing enough to make even olfactory pygmies such as ourselves salivate, with nasal sensing tissues only about four square centimetres in area, it is easy to imagine the effect of molecules from potential food on predators such as dogs whose nasal membranes are more than thirty times as large.

Indeed, polar bears can sniff out an appetizing dead seal more than twenty kilometres away while bloodhounds' noses are reported to be a million times more sensitive than ours. Not only can they follow a human trail by smelling the chemicals released from the skin cells that we continually shed, the dogs can even detect the minute genetically caused differences in smell signatures between two closely related people.

With predators so adept at sniffing them out, grazing animals have had to develop equally effective ways of detecting their enemies and communicating this knowledge to others in the herd. East African antelopes and gazelles regularly break off from browsing to sniff around for the scent of stalking lions or cheetahs. If they detect an approaching predator, antelopes such as springbok or impala release alarm chemical from special glands into the air. The scent message quickly spreads to the rest of the herd which immediately takes flight.

Animals use smells to communicate a variety of other messages apart from alarm. They use them to proclaim territorial rights. Felines ranging from lions to the domestic puss add a special marker to their urine which they then disperse over vegetation or furniture. Other animals use their faeces to disperse their personal scents in a similar fashion. Rabbits and badgers mark out their territories with piles of droppings, while white rhinos stamp in their faeces so that they can leave their personal signatures behind wherever they go.

Even more important perhaps than the ability to mark out one's territory is the need to attract a mate and this is a field where some animals have evolved strategies of spectacular cunning. For instance, male garter snakes find the female's sexual perfume so irresistible that dozens of them try to copulate with her at the same time but succeed only in forming a writhing mass in which little is accomplished. One or two crafty males then withdraw, at the same time secreting the female scent and thereby attracting the other males away from the female. While their competitors are still distracted, the Machiavellian males then quickly steal back to mate with the female.

Mammals also respond to sexual smells; dogs for example are able to detect the scent of any bitch on heat in the neighbourhood. The significance of such smells can often be understood by mammals of different species: grizzly and polar bears are strongly attracted by the odours of menstruating women.

As well as using their olfactory supersenses to communicate with one another, many animals also exploit their supersensitivity to minute environmental scents to help them find their way around. For example, when returning to spawn, salmon swimming in the ocean seem to be able to detect the distinctive scent of their natal stream well before reaching land. By following the scent towards its source they can locate the right river mouth and then swim upstream to the precise site where they were spawned.

Birds, too, use their sense of smell as an aid in navigation. Thus pigeons seem not only to be able to recognize the smells of their home area, they can even remember the scents associated with particular wind directions. When away from home, the birds seem to use the changes in relative strengths of different wind smells as guides to the direction home.

The pervasive use of smell language by other vertebrates and their remarkable ability to read the invisible signposts scattered throughout the natural environment suggests that we, too, may be far more sensitive to smell than we think. Experiments have been carried out showing that mothers could identify which T-shirts were worn by their own children and there is much other evidence supporting the notion that an unconscious awareness of each other's personal body odours plays an important part in cementing bonds between mother and child and between lovers. This was well understood before the advent of the twentieth-century Western consumer society and its neurotic obsession with personal hygiene; Napoleon is famously said to have written to Josephine from the battlefield, '*Ne te lave pas, je reviens.*'

Humans may also use a sense of smell to help them find their way around. For instance, when navigating across featureless tracts of polar ice, Eskimos, like pigeons, are reported to make use of the clues provided by the smells of different winds.

If a largely unconscious sense of smell now seems so important in human bonding and even in navigation, might it not also help to solve the riddle of dowsing success? This intriguing idea is not new – it was proposed many years ago by the constructive sceptic D.H. Rawcliffe.[4] He pointed out that dowsing used to be called 'water smelling' in many country districts, particularly in America, and suggested that some dowsers may be able to pick up very faint smells associated with underground water.

Rawcliffe's idea is supported by the fact that the prospectors of old looked for or smelt out rising vapours as a clue to the presence of underground mineral veins or water. We may recall that the Baroness de Beausoleil advised prospectors to look for 'the vapours that rise from mountains and valleys at dawn'. Even more to the point, as we have seen, the faults and fractures that are associated with mineral veins and flowing groundwater often act as channels that allow small quantities of the radioactive (but odourless) gas radon to rise up from below. Trace amounts of smelly gases such as methane may rise up along the same pathways, so it is quite possible that some dowsers may – quite unconsciously – be able to smell underground minerals, water and 'harmful earth rays'.

The notion that dowsers may exploit a hitherto unrecognized bloodhound-like supersense of smell is a challenging idea that has yet to be investigated. But if we continue to be guided by our vision of the Sphinx and the animal powers she represents, we see that dowsers may be able to utilize many more unconscious supersenses.

For instance, animals have developed remarkably sophisticated sensing systems for detecting wave motions produced by things in motion. In air or water, these waves travel as pressure disturbances, while in the solid Earth they travel as vibrations – such as earthquake waves.

The personal audio systems that we inherit from our vertebrate ancestors work in a somewhat similar fashion to ordinary microphones. Pressure waves in the air enter our earholes and cause the stretched membranes of our eardrums to vibrate at the same frequency as the air waves. A special system of bones then transmits the vibrations to a second, smaller, oval membrane, which because of its smaller size, vibrates more strongly than the eardrum itself. Finally, the vibrations are transmitted to a fluid-filled tube, the cochlea, and converted into nerve signals that pass to the cerebral cortex. Here, the signals are processed and presented to consciousness in the same mysterious way as information from our eyes and noses. As a result of this processing, we hear stronger, high-amplitude waves as louder noises and those of higher frequency as sounds of higher pitch.

Some animals have developed supersensitive hearing systems that can detect incredibly faint sounds. For instance, when foraging at night in the desert, the kangaroo rat lives in constant danger of being attacked by predators such as owls and rattlesnakes. But it rarely falls victim to them. Whereas our own hearing system only amplifies sounds about eighteen times, the rat's one amplifies sounds 100 times, enabling it to hear the faint sounds made by air rushing past the owl's wings or the snake's scales brushing against the sand.

Other animals can perceive frequencies far above the human range. While we can hear noises from about 20 hertz (vibrations per second) at the lower end to about 20,000 hertz at upper end, rats and mice can communicate at ultrasonic frequencies up to 100,000 hertz. Only their most high-pitched squeaks, though, are inaudible to eavesdropping cats, who can hear frequencies up to 70,000 hertz or so.

Some animals – for example, insectivorous bats that need to catch their prey at night and dolphins hunting for fish in the murky waters of South American rivers – use even higher frequencies in their amazing echolocation systems. From its larynx the bat emits pulses of ultrasound in frequencies up to 200,000 hertz. The sound pulses bounce off the flying insect prey and the echoes are collected by the bat's large pinnae (equivalents of our ear lobes). The sounds are converted into nerve impulses which are then processed by specialized areas of the animal's brain to yield an ever-changing sound picture of the scene.

The nearly blind river dolphins use a somewhat similar ultrasonic echolocation system, but because the sound waves travel through the bodies of fish almost as easily as through water, only being reflected by the bones, the dolphins must see an X-ray picture of their swimming prey.

We, too, seem to be able to use a primitive form of

echolocation if the need arises. Some blind people have developed a remarkable new sense known as facial vision.[5] They report feeling the presence of nearby objects as pressures on their cheeks. Experiments have shown that sound is responsible. People with this ability seem to hear the echoes of their own footsteps and other sounds returning from nearby objects. In their case, the nerve impulses from the ears are processed and presented to consciousness in the guise of physical pressure rather than noise.

The amazing capacity of the human brain to make constructive use of available sense data is highly relevant to the dowsing riddle. If blind individuals can develop an entirely new sense in this way, it would surely be easy for skilled dowsers to utilize appropriate supersensory information received by their unconscious minds.

Although nothing can be ruled out at this stage, it does seem unlikely that dowsers have developed bat-like echolocation systems using earth vibrations generated by their own footsteps. But could they instead exploit natural, low-frequency vibrations travelling through the Earth?

This exciting possibility comes to mind when we contemplate the uncanny abilities of many animals to sense in advance that an earthquake or volcanic eruption will happen. Before the great earthquake that devastated Messina, Sicily, in 1907, the city cats apparently all left town. A similar exodus of cats is said to have preceded the catastrophic eruption of Mt. Pelée in the French West Indian island of Martinique in 1902. Before a major earthquake hit Haicheng, China, in February 1975, local people reported that hibernating snakes emerged from their burrows and froze to death in the snow.[6] Before other earthquakes elephants and birds have shown alarm, horses have stampeded, cows have broken out of barns, and rats have emerged from sewers.

As we will see later, it seems that quite exotic supersenses may play a part in causing some of this strange behaviour before earthquakes. But some animals, at least, seem to pick up the low-frequency sound waves – infrasound – emitted by the ground as it trembles before earthquakes and others may detect the tremors directly.

The low-frequency (below 20 hertz) pre-earthquake air waves travel long distances and many animals, ranging from pigeons to elephants are probably able to hear them. Others may detect the minute pre-earthquake infrasonic earth tremors themselves. Snakes are supersensitive to such earth vibrations or microseisms. Sand scorpions can detect earth vibrations as small as one ten-thousandth of a millimetre[7] while ghost crabs, cockroaches and African mole-rats all seem capable of sensing minute earth vibrations at infrasonic and other frequencies.

At first sight it is difficult to see how a hypothetical supersensitivity to minute infrasonic earth vibrations, or the infrasound waves in air created by them, could help a dowser achieve success. Even if, like pigeons, elephants or snakes, dowsers could in some mysterious way sense these vibrations or waves, how could these deep rumblings from below help them to locate hidden geological faults?

Joseph Wüst, the German physical chemist whose investigations into possible links between dowsing and gamma rays have already been mentioned, tried to answer this question as early as the 1930s.[8] At that time he was collaborating in dowsing research with Joseph Wimmer, a physicist who subsequently ran a dowsing course for members of Hitler's dreaded SS during World War II. Wimmer and Wüst were dowsing in the Anatomical Institute at the University of Munich when they noticed a strange phenomenon. Their rods seemed to turn precisely at the times when the large extracting ventilator at the Institute was switched on or off. Wüst suspected that the dowsers might have picked up infrasound emanating from the ventilator.

In fact, the Earth beneath our feet is constantly vibrating, not only because of machinery such as Wüst's ventilator, but also as a result of natural phenomena. For instance ocean rollers breaking against coasts emit infrasound waves which not only pass through the atmosphere but also cause whole continents to vibrate. Heavy seas on the Norwegian coast can shake the ground as far away as Siberia, surf breaking against the western coasts of Scotland and Ireland can cause telegraph poles in Germany to hum, while storm waves crashing against the Atlantic coasts of France and Spain can make the Alps shiver.

Apart from ocean storms, there are many other natural sources of infrasonic earth vibrations: waterfalls, tectonic stress in the Earth's crust, the freezing and thawing of soil, rapid changes in barometric pressure, as well as more obvious causes such as earthquakes and volcanic eruptions. In populated areas human activities such as road and rail traffic, aircraft, industrial machinery, mining operations and so on constitute an ever-increasing source of earth vibrations. As a result of all this shaking, the ground is nearly always vibrating at infrasonic frequencies of 20 hertz and below.

But how might all this relate to dowsing? A key fact is that, like the larger earthquake waves, the amplitude of infrasonic microseisms depends on the rocks they are passing through. The vibrations are small in hard, crystalline rocks, larger in sedimentary rocks and reach a maximum in loose, water-saturated deposits such as river valley alluvium.

Of crucial significance for dowsers, these infrasonic vibrations are – as Wüst himself pointed out – amplified over faults and fractures. Where a fault lies hidden beneath a layer of water-saturated sediment, such as alluvial sands and gravels, the magnification may be particularly strong. Of equal interest is the fact that water or other fluids flowing in underground fissures can themselves give rise to earth vibrations at infrasonic and audio frequencies.

Geologists prospecting for underground water and engineers searching for leaks in underground water or gas pipes have learnt how to exploit these properties of microseisms. Thus geologists have discovered that narrow bands of enhanced microseismic activity can indicate the presence of water-bearing fissure systems in hard rocks.[9] Engineers have found that water or gas escaping from the pipe causes vibrations that they can detect with appropriate equipment.

Although there has been little research into the ways humans might sense these tiny vibrations, it is possible that some individuals may, like elephants, be able to hear the infrasonic air waves produced by the trembling ground. Joseph Wüst suggested that such infrasonic air waves might be picked up by human hairs and transmitted to the nerve cells around the hair roots.[10] Perhaps studies of the ways in which animals respond to these tiny vibrations might throw light on this question. But whatever the mechanism, if, like snakes or mole-rats, dowsers could detect the narrow bands of enhanced microseismic activity above certain faults, we would have at least one possible explanation for some of the remarkable dowsing achievements reported in chapters one and two.

8   Our Magnetic Supersense

One day in 1850, the citizens of Edinburgh witnessed one of the strangest spectacles of their lives. In the Firth of Forth a huge whale about 24 metres long had appeared close to the shore, spouting water 12 metres in the air. The monster was clearly in difficulties and soon the receding tide left the struggling animal stranded on the beach. A crowd gathered; some people fired shots at the whale while others attacked it with pitchforks. The unfortunate cetacean seems to have suffered this cruelty for some hours before dying from loss of blood.[1]

Aristotle was the first of many observers to comment on the strange tendency of whales and dolphins to beach themselves without apparent cause. Sometimes whole groups of cetaceans run aground together – in 1986 more than a hundred pilot whales headed straight for the shore near Reykjavik, Iceland, and died. In 1982, also in Iceland, a herd of 300 pilot whales swam towards the shore. However on this occasion the local people – friendlier towards whales than the citizens of Edinburgh had been – saved most of them by driving them back into deep water.[2]

Many people have put forward suggestions to explain the cetaceans' puzzling behaviour. Some have proposed that the creatures harbour suicidal tendencies, others that they enter shallow water to rub their itching skins or rest. Another idea has been that the whales suffer from parasitic infections of the inner ear which interfere with the operation of the animals' sonar echolocation systems. But when the evidence is carefully examined, none of these explanations really seem to make sense.

Attracted by this intriguing puzzle, Margaret Klinowska, of the Physiological Laboratory at the University of Cambridge, started to collect as much information as possible about whale strandings on the shores of the British Isles. Fortunately scientists at the British Museum (Natural History) in South Kensington had compiled comprehensive records which made it possible to distinguish live stranding events from the more numerous cases where currents or tides had carried the bodies of dead whales ashore.

In the course of her investigations, Margaret Klinowska decided to look at magnetic maps of those areas where the whales had stranded. Based on aeromagnetic surveys, such maps show contours in the same way as ordinary topographic maps do but here 'hills' represent places where the Earth's magnetic field is slightly stronger than normal and 'valleys' where it is weaker. What Klinowska noticed was quite extraordinary.[3, 4] Without exception, the live whales had run aground at places where the magnetic contours were perpendicular to the coastline. This suggested that the whales had been following the magnetic contours before they beached themselves. To do this, the animals would have to be capable of sensing minute changes in the intensity of the Earth's magnetic field.

This idea opens up exciting possibilities for dowsing theory. For whales are mammals like ourselves; they see, hear, smell and touch much as we do. Yet here we have evidence that these relatives of ours may have inbuilt magnetometers of the kind that geologists use when prospecting for hidden mineral lodes or archaeologists employ when they search for old foundations and graves. If we, too, possessed a magnetic supersense of this kind, many dowsers' claims would suddenly start to make sense.

Later on, we shall explore these ideas more fully. But before that, we need to look more closely at the wonder of nature that is the Earth's magnetic field, how whales and other animals seem mysteriously attuned to its subtle rhythms and changes, and how this helps them find their way around.

What causes the Earth's magnetic field and its variations in time and space? To answer this question – a true Earth mystery indeed – we need to picture our planet not as an inert globe spinning in space, but as a dynamic assemblage of interacting processes, powered by vast internal and external sources of energy.

The Earth formed by accretion of varied protoplanetary materials about 4,500 million years ago. Soon, energy from the impacts and from radioactive decay heated its interior. Heavy iron-rich matter sank to the centre to form a metallic core while gases including water vapour, carbon dioxide and nitrogen escaped to form an atmosphere and oceans.

Earth's internal energy sources, mainly radioactive isotopes of uranium, thorium and potassium, have kept the iron-rich metallic outer core so hot that despite losing heat to the cooler, outer part of the Earth, it has remained molten to this day. As the convecting molten metal spun with the rest of the Earth, it interacted in the manner of a dynamo with a small initial magnetic field to generate powerful electric currents that have circulated in the outer core ever since. These circulating electric currents generate the main part of the Earth's magnetic field in the same way that current flowing in a coil creates a magnetic effect.

But there is another component of the Earth's magnetic field that is sustained not by the internal energy of the Earth, but by the energy and influences of the sun. Short wavelength (ultraviolet and X-ray) photons from the sun have enough energy to knock electrons out of the atoms and molecules of the upper atmosphere. Although the positively charged ions so formed soon recombine with electrons again, during the daytime the bombardment of solar protons is continually producing new electrons and positive ions. So, during the daytime, but not at night, this part of the Earth's atmosphere – appropriately called the ionosphere – is an electrical conductor.

An electrical conductor in the upper atmosphere would not on its own create a new magnetic field. To do that, we would need to move the conductor through an existing field, thereby inducing a current to flow and a new field to form. Indeed, this is precisely what seems to happen. The sun's tidal effects on the upper atmosphere cause strong winds to blow – in other words the ionospheric conductor to move. During the day – but not at night, when it does not conduct – these winds interact with Earth's core-generated magnetic field to generate electric currents and new magnetism.

Even this is not the end of the story. As it builds up and declines each day, the ionospheric magnetic field induces electric currents to flow – and yet more new magnetism – in conductive parts of the Earth's crust such as sedimentary basins.

So we have two remarkable Earth dynamos, one in the outer core creating a large but relatively steady field and the other in the ionosphere producing a much smaller field that builds up during the hours of daylight. At any point on the Earth's surface, these two components combine to give the total field vector. We can picture this as an arrow, the length of which represents the field's intensity, pointing in the direction of the field. Near the Earth's north magnetic pole in northern Canada the arrow would be around 70,000 units long (each unit representing one nanotesla, the unit of magnetic field strength) and point almost vertically downwards. In Britain the arrow would be shorter – only about 47,000 units long – and point downwards, at an angle of between 60 and 70 degrees, its horizontal projection pointing towards the north magnetic pole. Near the geomagnetic equator the arrow would be shorter still and point horizontally towards magnetic north. At the south magnetic pole, off the coast of Antarctica, the arrow would be longer again and point almost vertically upwards.

At any particular place, our magnetic arrow would pulsate and sway in a similar way each day, as photons from the sun temporarily energize the ionospheric dynamo. In summer, when sunlight is more intense and days are longer, the daily rhythm would be stronger. Moreover, because the moon's tides also influence the ionospheric dynamo, our magnetic arrow's dance would also incorporate a monthly, lunar beat.

However, observations with magnetometers have shown that the regular performance of the magnetic vector is sometimes violently disturbed. On these occasions other unusual events may also occur – spectacular auroral displays and signs of exceptional activity on the sun. Until the 1960s, such events, known as magnetic storms were something of a mystery. Since then, satellite measurements have revealed what is really happening.

Instead of orbiting in an almost perfect vacuum, as scientists used to think, the Earth actually moves within a tenuous outer part of the sun itself, the solar corona. The outer part of the corona consists of very thin plasma – a gas of ionized particles, mainly protons and electrons – streaming away from the sun to form the solar wind. Under normal conditions, these charged particles are deflected away by the Earth's magnetic field long before they reach our planet. From time to time, though, the solar wind blows with unusual strength, pushing strongly against the Earth's magnetic field and squeezing the lines of magnetic force together. In the region of Britain, this initially causes the field vector to increase in magnitude and dip at a shallower angle. Breaking off from its usual rhythm, our magnetic field vector would pulsate and gyrate wildly for several hours until the magnetic storm blows itself out.

Magnetic storms of this kind are therefore caused by increases in the intensity of the solar wind. Such events often follow the solar flares that are most likely to occur when the sun is at its most active at the peak of the eleven-year sunspot cycle. Moreover, a persistent flare may be carried around by the roughly 28-day rotation of the Sun itself and thereby give rise to a regular series of monthly magnetic storms on Earth.

So now we can appreciate the complexity of the cosmic symphony to which the Earth's magnetic field vector dances, incorporating subtle themes generated not only by the Earth itself, but also by the moon and sun – literally music of the spheres.

Even this is not all. The Earth's outer core – which generates the main part of the Earth's field – has its own leisurely cycles. From time to time, changes in the circulation of the molten metal cause the main part of the Earth's field to decay and reverse its polarity. When this happens, the magnetic field vector at a locality in Britain would wobble, shrink, and then stagger upright again, but this time point in the opposite direction.

Since its birth the Earth has reversed its magnetic field thousands of times, the last persistent reversal being about 730,000 years ago, when the field acquired its present polarity. But a new reversal may be on its way. Measurements of the magnetism of 2,000-year old pots have shown that the Romans lived in a much stronger magnetic field than the one we know today. Should this decay continue, the field may reverse itself in about 2,000 years time. If so, the reversal process may prove an unpleasant experience for any human beings still living at that time; during the temporary absence of the Earth's protective magnetic sheath, carcinogenic high-energy particles from the sun will rain down on people like a hail of bullets.

As well as responding to the rhythms of the cosmos, the intensity of the Earth's magnetic field also varies from place to place, depending on the nature of the local rocks. It turns out that the critical factor is the nature and quantity of certain special crystals in the rocks, of which the most remarkable is the iron oxide mineral, magnetite.

Magnetite is a member of the spinel family of minerals, which are among the most symmetrical crystals known. If you look carefully at a large crystal of magnetite, you may notice that the crystal faces are those of a perfect octahedron, one of the five Platonic solids (the others being the tetrahedron, the cube, the regular dodecahedron and the icosahedron). In contemplating this marvellous symmetry, it is easy to feel that we are glimpsing one of the eternal, unchanging forms that, according to Plato, underlie the illusory world of appearances.

But the perfect symmetry of magnetite is not the mineral's most unusual aspect. Even more remarkable is the property commemorated in its name: its responsiveness to magnetic fields. In the Earth's field, ordinary, visible magnetite easily becomes magnetized: each crystal becomes a small magnet with its own field vector pointing in the same direction as that of the Earth. If a rock contains more such magnetite crystals than surrounding rocks, the effect is to increase the local intensity of the Earth's field and create a positive magnetic anomaly. Generally speaking, continents and the shallow shelf seas around them are characterized by magnetic topography of this kind – positive magnetic hills rising above a flattish magnetic plain. Here and there, steepish, often straight-edged cliffs would cut across the landscape – marking the locations of geological faults.

Continental rocks containing relatively large magnetite crystals – for example gabbros and other coarse-grained igneous rocks – are therefore finely attuned to the gyrations of the Earth's magnetic field. As the Earth's field vector pulses and sways in harmony with the rhythms of Earth and cosmos, so does the magnetism of the rock.

But not all crystals of magnetite behave in this way. If they are very tiny indeed – less than about 0.2 millimetres in diameter – their magnetic field vectors no longer dance to the symphony orchestrated by Gaia. Instead, each crystal's field vector remains rigid, frozen at the precise moment in time when the crystal solidified from its melt. If the Earth's field was reversed at that time, then the tiny crystals' field vectors will remain stuck in a reversed position today.

In fact, measurements with magnetometers have shown that many rocks, especially basalt volcanic lavas packed with tiny magnetite crystals, show reversed magnetization. The effect reduces the Earth's field strength locally, giving rise to a negative magnetic anomaly. Immediately next to the rock, the effect can be strong enough to cause a compass needle to point towards the south, just as it would have done when the rock cooled.

The discovery and mapping of ocean-floor basalts with reversed fossil magnetism played a key rôle in the geological revolution of the 1960s and 1970s when so many puzzling Earth mysteries – such as the matching of the Atlantic coastlines and fossils of Africa and South America – were solved. Magnetometers towed by ships showed long bands of alternating positive and negative magnetic anomalies parallel to the underwater mid-Atlantic ridge and other mid-oceanic ridge systems. At first scientists were baffled by these mysterious patterns. Then, in large part due to the efforts of three scientists – Harry Hess, of Princeton University and Drummond Matthews and Fred Vine, of the University of Cambridge, the penny dropped. The ocean floors were acting as giant tape recorders, each ocean ridge producing a pair of magnetic tapes that unwound away from the ridge in opposite directions. The first pair of magnetic troughs on either side of the ridge represented the last major period when the Earth's field was reversed while more distant magnetic troughs represented older magnetic reversals.

Having thereby understood the extraordinary seafloor-spreading mechanism by which Gaia continually transforms herself, Earth scientists were able to reconstruct the way the new ocean basins had grown, pushing the matching, broken edges of old continents apart and creating the face of the Earth we know so well today.

Now at last we have enough information to tackle the problem of why whales beach themselves. Recall that Margaret Klinowska made the surprising discovery that in Britain all recorded live whale strandings had occurred at places where magnetic contours ran roughly at right angles to the coastline. This suggested that the whales could have been using a magnetic supersense to follow the magnetic contours, and now we can see why they may have adopted this curious strategy. The regular pattern of magnetic ridges and troughs parallel to the mid-ocean ridges could provide travelling cetaceans with a ready-made system of motorways. To cruise along a motorway without effort, all a whale need do would be to follow the route that keeps the magnetic field strength unchanged.

However, should a whale misread the route map and get lost, this strategy could end in disaster. For once a whale strays away from the deep ocean basins and enters the shallow continental shelf seas around Britain, the magnetic contours no longer provide trouble-free motorways. The contours are quite likely to head straight for a beach – and as we have seen, so may the whale.

But what causes whales, brainy animals that they are, to misread their magnetic route maps in the first place? In search of the answer, Margaret Klinowska looked at magnetometer records to see if there was any correlation between the times of live whale strandings and the rhythms of the local magnetic field. She found something surprising. The whales tended to run aground on, or at least shortly after, the days when the regular daily magnetic rhythm of the ionospheric dynamo had been disturbed by solar influences.

Klinowska explained this by suggesting that as well as sensing Earth's magnetic topography, whales could also use Earth's pulsating magnetic field vector as a clock. They could thereby tune in to the rhythm of the ionospheric dynamo to obtain daily time signals. By swimming at constant speed along one of its magnetic motorways, a whale could tell roughly where it was. When the daily signal was obscured by solar influences, however, the whale might misjudge the distance it had travelled and continue on a road to disaster.

Since Klinowska first put forward her magnetic theory in the early 1980s, other groups of scientists have come up with independent evidence to support the concept that whales follow magnetic contours.[5, 6] Taken together, all these findings suggest that whales are almost unbelievably sensitive to magnetism. They seem able to sense changes in Earth's field strength as small as one nanotesla – remember that in Britain the total field strength is around 47,000 nanoteslas. This lets cetaceans detect the subtlest of geological features below the seafloor.

When swimming over the deep ocean basins, with the seafloor thousands of metres below them, dolphins or whales can detect not only the bands of reversed magnetism that we have already mentioned, they can also locate the great fractures known as transform faults that offset the mid-ocean ridges. But when cruising in the much shallower seas, floored by continental crust, that surround the continents, cetaceans can detect geological features with even greater precision. They can locate faults, fracture zones, mineral veins, igneous intrusions and so on. Whales must be superb potential dowsers, rivalling John Mullins or Hans Schröter in their seemingly uncanny ability to pinpoint hidden faults and fracture zones.

Leaving aside the quite serious possibility of training smaller cetaceans such as dolphins to dowse, the potential implications for dowsing theory are exciting. By following our vision of the Sphinx and the mysterious animal powers she represents we have found a family of mammals, close relatives of ourselves, who use a supersense that seems tailor-made to explain many dowsing successes.

But cetaceans are far from being the only animals that are sensitive to the Earth's magnetism. Since two American biologists discovered in 1975 that certain mud-dwelling bacteria have a magnetic sense,[7] the list of animals that can detect the Earth's magnetic field has grown year by year. Apart from whales, migratory sea-dwelling animals ranging from turtles to sharks, yellowfin tuna and salmon use a magnetic supersense to help them find their way on their marathon journeys. Biologists have trained yellowfin tuna to swim through plastic frames in response to changes in an applied magnetic field.[8]

Scientists have found that birds, too, make use of the Earth's magnetism. Significantly, not only migrants such as sparrows and blackcaps but also non-migratory species like robins have a magnetic sense. The bird whose magnetic sense has been investigated in the greatest detail, the homing pigeon, is also a non-migrant, being a domesticated variety of the rock dove, *Columbia livia*.

Unlike ocean-dwelling migrants such as whales, who are lucky enough to have access to a ready-made system of magnetic motorways, birds spend most of their time flying over continental terrain, where, as we have seen, the magnetic topography is less regular. So how do they cope? One strategy is to use the direction of dip of the Earth's field vector as a rough indication of north or south. But this ploy only works as long as the birds keep well away from the magnetic equator, where the magnetic vector is horizontal, and it seems that birds, like whales, fall back on the magnetic topography as a navigational aid.

In one experiment, for instance, scientists released pigeons from several sites, some of which were magnetically flat while others were on magnetic hills of varying heights. Birds released from the magnetically flat sites set off in the correct direction for home, while those released from the magnetic hills became confused and flew off at random.[9]

Like whales, birds too are affected by the magnetic storms caused by solar activity. During a storm, pigeons have difficulty in returning to their home lofts while young gulls and other birds also experience navigational problems. The magnetic storms probably cause trouble by interfering with the birds' perception of the magnetic landscape. To a flying bird, the increase in magnetic field strength associated with a storm would appear to be a new and confusing magnetic hill.

Such evidence suggests that almost every bird species studied has a magnetic sense. As there is similar evidence for whales and other mammals such as rodents[10] the implication is that most – possibly all – vertebrates have a supersense of this kind. In operation, the sense is likely to be highly complex, varying somewhat from species to species and fully comprehensible to a few experts only. For us, however, the important thing is that the supersense includes an ability to perceive the magnetic topography, the tiny place-to-place changes in the strength of the Earth's magnetic field.

In what form do animals perceive this magnetic information? Bearing in mind that we see things not as they are but in the form of a computer image produced by our brains, in principle there is no reason why animals should not consciously 'see' magnetic data. However, there are grounds for suspecting that the magnetic supersense of animals may not be a conscious one at all. Robin Baker, a zoologist at the University of Manchester who is an expert on animal navigation, has pointed out that when given the choice, animals prefer to use visual or other cues rather than their sense of magnetism.[11] Homing pigeons, for example, often prefer to wait for the sun to appear rather than rely on their sense of magnetism to guide them safely home. The magnetic sense is clearly near the bottom of a preference ranking that Baker has suggested may also correspond to a hierarchy of consciousness. At the top of this hierarchy would be preferred, most conscious senses such as vision, while at the bottom would be least conscious – probably unconscious – senses like magnetism.

The notion that the magnetic supersense of animals may be an unconscious one raises the exciting possibility – with all its potential implications for dowsing – that we too have a hidden sense of this kind. Since 1979 Robin Baker has carried out many experiments with students that have demonstrated, to his own satisfaction at least, that we do indeed have an unconscious magnetic sense.

In Baker's earlier experiments[12, 13, 14] he treated his human subjects rather as if they were homing pigeons. In several tests, students were first fitted out with special electromagnetic helmets. Some of the students wore helmets that exposed their heads to magnetic field vectors pointing to the right, others wore similar but left-pointing magnetic helmets, while a control group of students wore inactive helmets that left the students exposed to the Earth's unaltered magnetic field. The students were then taken by bus from their home school or campus along twisting routes to various 'release sites' where they pointed to or otherwise indicated their own estimates of 'home'.

The results of many such experiments told the same story. While the control groups of students indicated 'home' direction with surprising accuracy, those wearing magnetically active helmets could not do so. Moreover, the home directions indicated by students wearing right-directing magnetic helmets were displaced to one side of the true 'home', while the directions indicated by those wearing left-directing magnetic helmets were displaced to the other side. Here, surely, was a clear demonstration that, like whales and pigeons, we too have an unconscious magnetic supersense.

Following Baker's pioneering studies, other investigators at universities in the USA, Australia and Britain carried out similar experiments. The results were most intriguing. According to Baker[15], when considered together, the findings of the other workers provide powerful statistical confirmation that we do indeed have a magnetic sense. However the investigators themselves have generally disputed this in their own conclusions.

While the detailed statistical arguments on both sides are too technical for non-specialists to appreciate, one can make a relevant observation. In the past, whenever some bold individual has proposed an entirely new concept – whether it be the great antiquity of the Earth, the arrival of meteorites from space, or the remorseless shifting of the continents beneath our feet – the ultra-cautious spirits of the scientific world have at first always rejected the new idea. As the proposed human magnetic sense is certainly a subversive concept of this kind, Baker clearly has history on his side.

Despite many orthodox scientists' hostility to the notion of a human magnetic sense, Baker has continued to study it. He has claimed that we use our sense of magnetism in many everyday situations even when we can see. For example, when exploring in woodland, people seem to use their magnetic supersense as an aid in judging direction and distance when the sun is of little use as a directional guide – either too high in the sky or hidden by cloud.[16]

Impressive recent support for the idea has come from studies of children's navigational prowess made by Gai Murphy, another zoologist at the University of Manchester.[17] Her experiments were simplicity itself. Wearing opaque goggles, each child was first spun round in a swivel chair. When the chair stopped, facing in one of eight possible directions (north, north-east, east and so on), the child had to name the direction it thought it was facing.

The results showed that boys and girls estimate direction in completely different ways. Although both sexes first develop a sense of direction when about eleven years old, thereafter – according to Murphy – boys and girls diverge. Boys, thinking themselves clever, try to calculate their position by monitoring the rotation of the spinning chair. They fail hopelessly in this task and, in Murphy's experiments, never managed to develop a good sense of direction. Girls, on the other hand, excelled at direction-finding – unless they wore a magnet at eye level, attached to the elastic strap of their goggles.

Gai Murphy concluded that the girls achieved success by modestly recognizing that they could not keep track of the chair's rotations and therefore guessing instead. In so doing, they unconsciously used their hidden magnetic supersense, thereby outperforming the overconfident, calculating boys.

The sexually stereotyped behaviour by Murphy's boy and girl subjects does seem surprising and it would be interesting to see the results of similar experiments repeated by workers at other universities. Nevertheless, taken at face value, the Manchester University findings have immense significance for dowsing theory and practice. Not only is there evidence that, like whales and pigeons, we too have a hidden magnetic supersense, but Gai Murphy's swivel chair experiments with children suggest the precise mechanism whereby walking dowsers may unconsciously move their rods in response to magnetic cues.

Murphy's children were only able to use the magnetic information received by their brains if they stopped calculating, relaxed and simply guessed. This brings to mind the surprising process of hand sight discussed in the last chapter: by guessing – and thereby exploiting an unconscious sensitivity of our skin to thermal infra-red rays – we can learn to 'see' different colours with our fingers.

Now, if dowsers agree upon one thing, it is that someone who thinks or calculates while dowsing will not succeed. Remember William Cookworthy's comment, quoted in chapter one, that the dowsing rod 'constantly answers in the hands of peasants, women and children who hold it simply without puzzling their minds with doubts or reasonings'. Gai Murphy's findings harmonize perfectly with centuries-old dowsing lore, suggesting that the same unconscious magnetic information retrieval process may be involved in both direction finding and dowsing.

But before we develop this idea further, there is an obvious question to be tackled: how do animals – including, it seems, ourselves – actually detect minute magnetic changes? The first clue to a possible answer came in the mid 1970s when the group of American scientists who first discovered the magnetic bacteria started to investigate these tiny creatures more closely.[18] They found something very odd. Each bacterium contained a chain of about twenty tiny octahedral or cubic crystals of magnetite, the crystals being only about 50 nanometres (billionths of a metre) across. The crystal chains lay along the axes of the bacteria, moreover the north-seeking magnetic poles of each little crystal all pointed in the same direction: along the axes of the organisms.

The scientists had discovered that the magnetic bacteria do not merely, like the mariners of old, have magnetite compasses, they *are* compasses. The Earth's magnetic field exerts sufficient torque on the crystal chain within each bacterium to align the whole organism along the direction of the local magnetic field vector. Here, truly, is a case of the compass steering the ship.

Such an arrangement does, however, leave the bacterium with only two options. It can either travel in the direction of the Earth's magnetic field vector or on a diametrically opposite bearing. But this suits the simple lifestyle of these little mud dwellers very well. Because they must live at the right depth in the mud, one of the few things the bacteria need to know is which direction is up and which down. Being too small to feel the Earth's gravity, they have turned to the Earth's magnetism as an alternative. In the Massachusetts swamps where they were first discovered, the Earth's magnetic field vector dips steeply downwards. So if a bacterium moves in the direction of the vector, it is going down and if it moves in the opposite direction, it is going up.

Following the discovery of chains of tiny magnetite crystals – termed magnetosomes – in mud-dwelling (and later soil-dwelling) bacteria, scientists found deposits of magnetic material in many of the other animals that seem to have a magnetic supersense. While in some cases the nature and rôle of this magnetic material remains dubious, in the case of at least one vertebrate, chinook salmon, scientists have found quantities of magnetosomes similar to those in bacteria.

If a single magnetosome can provide only crude magnetic information, many acting together could have evolved into a sophisticated magnetic sense organ, just as billions of years of evolution turned simple photosensitive cells into the advanced vertebrate retina. A group of American scientists have in fact shown that one species, the yellowfin tuna – which can perform tricks in response to magnetic cues – may have a supersensitive magnetic sensor of just this kind.[19, 20] The scientists found that a sinus in the dermethmoid bone of the fish's skull contained perhaps 85 million tiny magnetite crystals. If organized in magnetosomes and integrated into one combined sense organ, the scientists calculated, the tuna's minute magnetite-based sensor could detect changes in the Earth's field strength as small as one nanotesla. Barely credible magnetic sensitivity of this kind – just what is demonstrated by whales and pigeons – would give the tuna superb dowsing abilities.

So do we, who also seem to have a magnetic supersense, also have a magnetite-based magnetic sense organ of this kind? In 1983 Robin Baker and his colleagues at the University of Manchester found magnetic material in the very thin bones of the human sphenoid/ethmoid sinus complex in the front of the skull.[21] Intriguingly, this is a similar anatomical position to that occupied by the tuna's probable magnetic sensor.

But, interesting though his discovery was, Baker was unable to show that his magnetic material included tiny magnetite crystals of the kind that some animals seem to use in magnetic sensing. So, during the 1980s and early 1990s, most scientists remained unconvinced that there really is a magnetite-based magnetic sensing apparatus within our heads.

Then, in May 1992, three Californian scientists – the Caltech husband-and-wife team Joseph Kirschvink and Atsuko Kobayashi-Kirschvink, together with Barbara Woodford of the University of Southern California – announced a detailed set of findings that settled the question once and for all.[22-24] Using tissue from seven human brains, the researchers managed to separate and identify minute magnetite crystals of precisely the same kind as had been found in salmon, tuna and other animals. The crystals seemed to be distributed throughout the brain, with the highest concentration in the meninges, the tissue that surrounds the brain. They estimated that there were around seven *billion* magnetite crystals in the average human brain. As the only logical rôle for such crystals lies in magnetic field detection, it seems that the physical basis of our magnetic supersense has at last been revealed.

But magnetite-based systems may not be the only magnetic sense organs we possess. It now seems likely that we also have other magnetic sensing equipment based on completely different physical principles – the abstruse notions of quantum physics.

Credit for stimulating scientific thought along these new lines must go to that excellent organization, the BBC. For it was after watching a BBC TV *Horizon* documentary on the newly discovered magnetic sense of birds in 1977 that M.J.M. Leask, an Oxford physicist, turned his mind to the problem of how a bird could possibly detect a magnetic field as small as that of the Earth.[25] After much thought, he came up with the ingenious idea that birds' retinas might double up as magnetic sense organs.

Leask based his theory on the fact that in the basic process of vision, molecules of rhodopsin or other pigments in the photosensitive cells of the retina undergo changes when they absorb photons of a specific energy. Leask calculated that when this happens, the changes in the rhodopsin molecule should also depend on the surrounding magnetic field. As long as light is falling on them, therefore, the photosensitive cells of the bird's retina could receive information about the direction of the Earth's magnetic field vector in relation to the axis of the cell. Because the axes of the millions of photosensitive retinal cells all point in slightly different directions, taken together the bird's retina could be a highly sensitive magnetic sense organ.

For a number of years, Leask's proposal remained in a kind of limbo. Then, in the mid 1980s, workers in the Department of Zoology at the University of Frankfurt tested the theory in a series of experiments with pigeons.[26, 27] They exposed anaesthetized pigeons to computer-generated magnetic fields that had the effect of rotating the Earth's magnetic field vector with respect to the stationary birds. At the same time the investigators monitored the electrical activity of single nerve cells in the parts of the pigeon's brain that process visual information received by the retina.

The results were remarkable. As the magnetic field vector swung round, individual nerve cells burst into activity and continued to fire as long as the field vector remained within a few degrees of a specific direction. This phenomenon only took place when the pigeon's retina was illuminated; in complete darkness there was no response.

These findings showed that Leask's brainwave was not just a clever idea, it actually corresponds to reality. In pigeons, at any rate, the pigment-containing photosensitive cells of the retina do indeed detect the direction of the Earth's field in the way that Leask suggested. The magnetic information is processed in the optical regions of the pigeon's brain. Here, groups of adjacent nerve cells, which correspond to groups of neighbouring photosensitive cells in the retina, fire when their retinal colleagues are stimulated by particular orientations of the Earth's magnetic field vector.

But Leask's mechanism may not be the only way in which our eyes can detect changes in the Earth's magnetic field. In 1982, K. Schulten, a German physical scientist, also using quantum theory, outlined a scheme whereby such magnetic changes could influence certain biochemical reactions.[28, 29] Following this proposal, several workers wondered if this concept could explain some surprising discoveries that had been accumulating concerning the effects of magnetic changes on our biological rhythms.

Many people have experienced the disturbance to their biorhythms known as jet lag – the tiredness and disorientation that may follow a long jet flight. People suffer most from jet lag after a long flight to the east, somewhat less after flying west, and not at all after flying north or south. The explanation for these weird effects seems to lie in the activities of the pineal gland – that tiny organ inside our heads that Descartes believed to be the abode of the soul.

The pineal produces a hormone called melatonin which – amongst other things – plays a part in making us feel sleepy. In response to signals from a still-mysterious internal clock in a neighbouring part of the brain called the hypothalamus, the pineal's output of melatonin fluctuates daily, peaking at night when we therefore feel sleepy. This system therefore works well as long as we remain in the same time zone – after flying north or south within the zone, the melatonin peak still falls at the right time. But when we fly east or west to a new time zone, the melatonin peaks continue to follow their old rhythm, making us feel sleepy during the day instead of at night.

Why do we suffer most from jet lag after flying east? It turns out that if left on its own our internal clock in the hypothalamus keeps to a roughly 25-hour cycle. It is tuned to a 24-hour period by receiving signals from the eyes, to which it is linked by nerve fibres branching off from the main optic nerve. When flying west with the sun, we experience a longer day, not so different from our natural 25-hour cycle, and may suffer little jet lag. But when flying east, we experience a compressed day, much shorter than the 25-hour cycle, and are more likely to suffer from melatonin-induced jet lag.

But what are the signals that synchronize our internal clocks with the 24-hour cycle of the solar day? Light certainly plays a part – experiments with humans and other animals have shown that exposure to bright light in the early morning can do the trick. However, evidence has recently accumulated that daily magnetic signals may also be involved. Several workers have now shown that in a variety of species, artificial alterations in the strength of the Earth's magnetic field affect the production of melatonin.[30] Oddly enough, this effect takes place not only in the pineal gland, the main source of melatonin, but in one species at least (the quail) in the retina itself.

That the vertebrate retina should produce melatonin is at first sight surprising because, apart from inducing sleep, the hormone has other effects including the destruction of visual photosensitive cells in the presence of light. However, the hormone also has a beneficial effect in the eye – it helps us to see in the dark. This could explain why, despite its destructive effects, melatonin is produced in the retina.

The evidence that animals require melatonin at night – to induce sleep, or improve night vision, according to lifestyle – could explain why they may have evolved the strategy of synchronizing their melatonin production with the daily magnetic pulsations produced by Earth's ionospheric dynamo. During the daytime, magnetic pulsing could inhibit the production of melatonin but permit higher levels of the hormone at night, just when it is needed.

Professor Gertrud Cremer-Bartels, of the eye clinic at the University of Munster in Germany, has come up with some intriguing results that are not only consistent with this idea, but also provide powerful evidence that human beings can indeed respond to small magnetic changes.[31] She found that artificial alterations in the strength of the Earth's field made the night vision of a group of male students worse. This is consistent with the idea that small changes in the Earth's magnetic field inhibit the production of melatonin, possibly by means of a quantum-mechanical mechanism akin to the one proposed by Schulten.

Taken together, the implications of all these findings are revolutionary. It now seems that our heads may house several supersensitive magnetic measuring devices, responding to tiny changes in the Earth's magnetic field in various ways. The pineal gland and retina may vary their melatonin output – and thereby regulate our biorhythms – not only with the intensity of light, but also with the complex rhythms of the Earth's magnetic field vector, as it dances to the music of the cosmos. The retina on its own, possibly backed up by a magnetite-based system for use in darkness, may monitor tiny place-to-place magnetic changes as we walk around and relay the data to the brain for use in navigation – and dowsing. So, far from being undetectable by humans, as orthodox science has traditionally claimed, it now seems that the magnetism of Gaia plays a central rôle in our lives.

9 The Electromagnetic Link

Stimulated by Jung's vision of the Sphinx, we have already identified a remarkable set of unconscious, animal-like supersenses that successful dowsers might use – sensitivities to thermal infra-red waves, supersmell, earth vibrations and, especially, magnetism. Could there be others?

One possibility that has been a longstanding favourite with dowsers themselves is a sensitivity to electromagnetic radiation. As we have seen, dowsers certainly respond to radiation in one band of the electromagnetic spectrum – visible light. But when dowsers invoke electromagnetic rays to explain their successes, they are not thinking of ordinary light waves (between 400 and 700 nanometres long) but rather microwaves and radio waves ranging in length from a centimetre or so to thousands of kilometres.[1, 2]

Could there be any truth in such ideas? As their name suggests, we can think of electromagnetic waves as both electric and magnetic oscillations. The great English experimentalist, Michael Faraday (1791–1867) first showed how oscillating electric and magnetic fields could propagate themselves indefinitely. The oscillating electric field would produce an oscillating magnetic field that would in turn produce another oscillating electric field and so on, the process continuing for ever. The two fields, electric and magnetic, would push each other along in the form of an electromagnetic wave travelling at the speed of light. Later scientific geniuses, including James Clerk Maxwell, Max Planck and Albert Einstein – put Faraday's ideas into mathematical form and reformulated the whole package in terms of quantum theory.

For our purposes though, Faraday's simple concept of electromagnetic waves as electric and magnetic oscillations pushing each other along will suffice. It is at once obvious that if animals and dowsers can sense very small changes in the strength of the Earth's magnetic field, they might also be able to detect variations in the magnetic component of the Earth's natural electromagnetic fields.

For it is now known that our planet generates a whole range

of different electromagnetic fields. At very low frequencies, lightning flashes in tropical thunderstorms cause pulsations of the Earth's magnetic field at the rate of about 10 oscillations per second (10 Hertz). These pulsations produce very long radio waves comparable in span with the Earth's circumference. The waves become trapped in the waveguide between the Earth's surface and the ionosphere; they may therefore continue to propagate almost indefinitely. Such very long, low frequency electromagnetic waves, known as Schumann resonances, are the Earth's characteristic radio transmissions.

Although the rate of 10 oscillations per second is very slow in comparison with the frequencies used by radio and TV transmitters, it is extremely fast compared with the daily and monthly oscillations of the Earth's magnetic field vector that we looked at in the last chapter. So, from the long-term point of view, we can regard the Schumann electromagnetic waves as high-pitch vibrations of the Earth's magnetic field vector, complementing the vector's more sedate gyrations as it dances to the music of the cosmos.

Linked as they are with the Earth's magnetic field, the Schumann electromagnetic resonances show similar daily variations, peaking in the late afternoon and remaining low at night. So could animals and humans have learned to tune in to these very long electromagnetic waves to adjust their biological clocks? There is some intriguing evidence to support this idea. In a classic experiment, R. Wever in Germany[3] studied the biorhythms of men living in an underground bunker, exposed to constant lighting conditions but shielded as far as possible from the Earth's magnetic and electromagnetic fields. After a few days, the sleep and activity patterns of the magnetically deprived men were gravely disturbed. By contrast, a control group of men living in an otherwise similar but electromagneti-cally unshielded bunker continued to sleep in regular cycles – though in this experiment the cycle's period increased to its natural length of about 25 hours. In another experiment, Wever found that an artificially produced 12-hour-on 12-hour-off schedule of Schumann-type (10 Hertz) electromagnetic fields could synchronize drifting human biological clocks to a 24-hour cycle.

Such results imply that the Earth's natural electromagnetic broadcasts and their daily variations play a vital part in our lives. It is therefore conceivable that dowsers could tune in to the Schumann resonances. If so, how could this help them to achieve dowsing success? Professor Michael Persinger, of Laurentian University, Ontario, has pointed out that the amplitude of Schumann waves can increase greatly over electrical conductors such as water-filled fissures and ore bodies.[4] So a dowser able to tune in the Earth's natural low-frequency radio transmissions would have yet another water- and mineral-finding arrow in his quiver.

But the Schumann band is not the only frequency range at which Gaia broadcasts to the cosmos. Solar-driven motions of air masses and electrical storms in Earth's atmosphere generate electrical oscillations which produce radio waves kilometres long, vibrating thousands of times per second. As in the case of the much longer Schumann waves, the received strength of these atmospherics varies from place to place, depending on the conductivity beneath the ground.

Indeed, geophysicists have developed techniques for locating conductive ore bodies and water-filled fissures that exploit these properties of atmospherics. One method depends on the fact that, confined as they are in the waveguide between the Earth's surface and the ionosphere, the radio atmospherics are normally partially polarized in a horizontal plane. But over conductors such as ore bodies or water-filled fissures, the plane of polarization tilts towards a vertical position.

A supersensitivity to these radio atmospherics could therefore be of great use to a dowser. One of the scientists participating in the recent German dowsing investigation, Professor G. Ruhenstroth-Bauer of the Max Planck Institute for Biochemistry in Munich, has demonstrated a statistical link between exposure to radio atmospherics and the onset of a variety of ailments – epileptic seizures, heart attacks and sudden deafness.[5, 6, 7] So, if the human brain and body are adversely affected by the strength of radio atmospherics, it is conceivable that some dowsers have learned to unconsciously tune in to these Gaian broadcasts and use variations in the intensity or degree of polarization of the waves as a guide to the presence of underground ore bodies or groundwater.

If dowsers could in principle respond to radio waves much longer than light, as well as light waves themselves, might they also be able to sense electromagnetic waves a thousand times shorter and more energetic than light waves: gamma rays? Could they perhaps also sense the other forms of high-energy, ionizing radiation: alpha and beta rays?

Some animals, for instance planarian worms, have apparently shown sensitivity to gamma rays[8] so a human sensitivity to ionizing radiation is certainly conceivable. At all events there is evidence that animals may be affected by a natural consequence of ionizing radiation – ionized air. When animals or humans inhale positively charged 'small ions' (consisting typically of a cluster of up to eight water molecules with a single positive charge) suspended in the air they may experience what is known as a 'serotonin stimulation syndrome'.[9] The positive ions somehow increase the production of the neurotransmitter serotonin in the midbrain: this can cause animals to show disturbed behaviour and humans to display symptoms such as nervousness, nausea and vomiting. Perhaps the stories that dowsers such as Barthelemy Bléton actually became ill over underground water contain some truth after all.

A sensitivity to ionizing radiation or ionized air would certainly be of the greatest use to a dowser. As we saw in chapter three, radon, which together with its daughters emits ionizing radiation such as gamma rays, often rises up along certain faults, mineral veins and water-filled fissures. Hidden faults and fractures may therefore betray their presence by tell-tale belts of gamma rays and other ionizing radiation accompanied by ionized air.

In theory, there is no reason why the list of subtle Earth influences which dowsers might sense should end with ionizing radiation. Various people have suggested that dowsers may respond to electric field changes,[10] variations in the electrical capacity[11] or resistance of the ground beneath their feet.[12] But changes in Earth's electric field depend chiefly on atmospheric processes and can tell a dowser little about what lies underground. Knowledge of underground electrical capacity or resistance, on the other hand, could be of great value to a dowser searching for water. However, as Yves Rocard pointed out to me when I visited him in Paris, these electrical parameters are passive properties, unlike active Earth influences such as magnetism or microseisms. Geophysicists wanting to measure them have to pass electric currents through the ground. Since dowsers do not emit electric shocks from their feet, it is very difficult to see how they could sense changes in these passive underground properties as they walk along.

The objections to these particular ideas do not rule out the existence of other unconscious supersenses which dowsers might use. But, by following Jung's vision of the Sphinx and her world of unconscious animal powers, we have already identified enough possibilities to suffice for the present. What we need to do now is to consolidate some of these ideas into a unified theory of dowsing.

The central premise of the theory is that our brains receive far more sense data about the world than we realize. Some of this information is collected by conventional sense organs, while other data – for instance magnetic information – is received and passed to the brain by mechanisms that scientists are only just beginning to understand.

In both cases, however, the information is not presented to consciousness. Presumably it is not useful enough to be included within the limited quantity of data that our conscious minds can handle at one time. Yet the information is still there in the background should we ever need it.

For instance, when exploring in forest or woodland under a cloudy sky, with nothing visible to guide us, we might unconsciously fall back on magnetic information, just as other animals seem to do. Robin Baker has argued that we do in fact use magnetic cues in these circumstances.[13]

Dowsers have traditionally operated in conditions of precisely this kind. If mineral veins or water-filled fissures were visible, there would be no need to resort to dowsing to find them. So, in default of visual or other conventional sensory information, skilled dowsers unconsciously tap the flow of magnetic and other supersensory data that is continually streaming into their brains.[14] They seem to do this by a kind of unconscious guesswork, similar to the brain processes that take place when people 'see with their hands' or when the girls in Gai Murphy's swivel chair experiments succeeded in guessing the direction they were facing.

Viewed from this new perspective, far from being a naïve or foolish procedure as sceptics allege, traditional dowsing turns out to be a highly intelligent solution to the problem of locating things hidden beneath the ground. When searching for faults or water-filled fissures, a skilled dowser like Hans Schröter would simply be making use of all available sensory information, instead of restricting himself – as geologists do – to a particular set of visual data interpreted in a stereotyped way.

If these ideas turn out to be correct, the implications will extend far beyond dowsing itself. There will be scientific confirmation that human beings have immense reserves of sensory capacity, that we can all learn to extend our awareness of our environment, including other human beings and animals as well as the geological features of the Earth.

10   Dowsing Explained?

Like all good scientific hypotheses, the supersensory theory of dowsing success makes testable predictions. It asserts that dowsers' rod movements should correlate with supersensory cues, such as small magnetic changes, as well as with normal sensory cues. Moreover there should be evidence that dowsers have located successful sites at places where relevant supersensory cues were available.

So is there any hard evidence that dowsers' rod movements do in fact correlate with small magnetic changes? As the theory predicts that other sensory cues will also trigger dowsing responses, we would not expect a perfect link between magnetic feature and dowsing response. However, if dowsers do make use of a magnetic supersense, we would expect to find some correlation.

One of the first scientists of modern times to present relevant data was that pioneer of dowsing research, Dr Joseph Wüst. In 1941 Wüst claimed, 'I now have irrefutable evidence that those places where the intensity of the horizontal component of the Earth's magnetic field varies by more than about 100 gammas (nanoteslas) per metre induce a dowsing response.'[1] Then, in 1949, Solco Tromp claimed that in mountainous areas, dowsers' rod movements correlated with magnetic anomalies. He supported this claim with experiments of his own, carried out at the Geological Institute in Leiden.[2]

However, Tromp later took the view that the correlation of dowsers' rod movements with magnetic data was a secondary consequence of their physiological response to other factors – for instance changes in soil resistivity.[3] Then he changed his mind again, claiming that thermal infra-red rays, not magnetism or soil resistivity initiate the dowser's response.[4]

Here we see the weakness of Tromp's physiological theory of dowsing: a single factor has to explain all dowsing successes. According to the supersensory theory, this is not the case so there is no need to keep changing one's mind as new experimental data reveal correlations with different geophysical signals. When searching for mineral veins in mountainous areas, dowsers may use their magnetic supersense, but when looking for water in flat regions where no magnetic cues are available, they may rely on other supersensory data.

If Solco Tromp was somewhat fickle in his support for the notion that dowsers respond to magnetic anomalies, that certainly cannot be said of another well-known dowsing investigator, the French physicist Yves Rocard (1903–1992), father of Michel Rocard, former French Prime Minister. Recognized as one of the most brilliant French scientists of his generation, Yves Rocard's researches had applications ranging from the suspension of the Citroën 2CV car to the stability of bridges. Rocard also contributed towards the development of the French atomic and hydrogen bombs.

During World War II Yves Rocard played a vital rôle in the Resistance movement, supplying priceless technical information to the British Secret Intelligence Service, MI6. On one occasion, R.V. Jones, head of science in MI6, was trying to obtain details of a radio navigational beam station that the Germans had set up in France, apparently to guide their fighter aircraft at night. The British were planning to parachute in an officer to find out details. But Rocard managed to smuggle out such excellent technical information that this risky venture was deemed unnecessary.

In 1945 Rocard was appointed director of the Laboratoire de Physique at the Ecole Normale Supérieure in Paris, one of the most prestigious scientific posts in France. Although he had long suspected that magnetism played a part in dowsing, it was not until 1962 that he presented his ideas in the form of a book, entitled *Le Signal du Sourcier*[5], arguing that dowsers' reactions were responses to small magnetic anomalies – bumps in the magnetic landscape. Supporting his claims with experiments of his own, in which walking dowsers apparently moved their rods in response to artificial magnetic anomalies as small as 70 nanoteslas, Rocard claimed that the anomalies in some way triggered a dowsing reflex.

While his book captured the imagination of the French public, the inevitable limitations of a one-man effort like Rocard's meant that his claims did not convince his scientific colleagues. But in 1971 the notion that dowsers can respond to magnetic cues received more substantial scientific support. When Duane Chadwick conducted the dowsing studies at Utah State University mentioned in chapter five, as part of the project he carried out detailed magnetic surveys of the test paths after the dowsers had walked along them.[6] As a professional scientist, with funding from the Federal Government, Chadwick had access to expensive state-of-the-art technology – caesium vapour magnetometers, which enabled him to accurately measure tiny place-to-place changes in the total strength of the Earth's magnetic field. To achieve unambiguous results, he compared readings of a probe magnetometer, pulled on a sledge along the paths, with simultaneous readings of a stationary magnetometer. In this way he could make sure that the magnetic changes measured along the paths corresponded to the actual magnetic topography, and were not influenced by any variations of the Earth's field with time.

Chadwick carried out his first magnetic experiment in an apple orchard in Logan, Utah. Using simple L-rods made from wire coat-hangers, twelve students, most of whom had not dowsed before, walked one at a time along a 50-metre test path between the apple trees. The students dropped small wooden blocks to mark the places where their rods moved. After each dowser had completed the course, an experimenter removed the blocks so as to provide no cues for the next dowser.

After all the students had completed the first test, an experimenter surveyed the magnetic topography. Apart from three shallow magnetic troughs, about 10 nanoteslas deep, at intervals along the path, the magnetic landscape was flat. The dowsers' rod movements tended to avoid the magnetically flat regions, clustering in the magnetic troughs.

Then Chadwick created an artificial magnetic anomaly by burying a thin iron rod about 30 metres from the start of the course, hiding it in such a way that no trace was visible at the surface. The students walked over the course again, one by one, as before, and a second magnetic survey was made. This showed that the iron rod had created a very deep magnetic chasm, about three metres wide. When the positions of the dowsers' new responses were plotted on a graph showing the magnetic measurements, a striking pattern emerged. The dowsers' responses had clustered together in several groups, the two largest clusters corresponding with the margins of the new magnetic chasm, while other clusters seemed to correlate with the small magnetic troughs.

These surprising results encouraged Chadwick to carry out further magnetic experiments at other locations. For his next site, he chose a trailer (caravan) park which possessed the advantage of having no trees to provide visual cues for the dowsers. Twenty students walked along a 20-metre path: about 8 metres from the start Chadwick had produced an artificial magnetic anomaly by burying a hidden iron rod in the soil. After measuring the positions of the dowsers' responses, the investigators carried out a magnetic survey in the same way as before. The magnetic landscape was rather similar to the one that student dowsers had encountered in the apple orchard: flattish, though with several small bumps and hollows and a deep magnetic chasm surrounding the buried iron rod.

Once again, the dowsers' rod movements showed a strong link with the magnetic topography, their responses clustering on the far edge of the magnetic chasm and also appearing to correlate with the other smaller magnetic features (see diagram overleaf).

Following these two intriguing sets of results, Duane Chadwick conducted further magnetic tests at two other sites: North Logan City Park and along the banks of the Potomac River in Lorton, Virginia. However, as Yves Rocard subsequently pointed out, in both places the magnetic landscapes were unsuitable for investigating possible links between dowsers' responses and small magnetic changes. In North Logan City Park, the dowsers walked through a sequence of huge magnetic anomalies that extended across the whole site. By contrast, the riverside site was magnetically flat, with the exception of small magnetic disturbances at the end of the dowsers' walk. Despite these unpropitious circumstances, inspection of Chadwick's results still shows some apparent correlation between dowsing responses and magnetic changes.

In another magnetic experiment, Chadwick measured the responses of a single dowser, walking along the same test path – but with variable starting positions – on different occasions. In this way, Chadwick reasoned, it might be possible to exploit the consistency of an individual's dowsing response. The results corroborated those of the other experiments: the dowsers' responses showed an uncanny relationship to the magnetic topography.

In almost all the Utah State University experiments, one thing stood out. While dowsers' responses seemed to correlate with small magnetic ridges and troughs, they showed a different relationship to the much larger anomalies produced by the buried iron rods. Instead of clustering directly above the buried rod, the dowsing responses tended to fall into two clusters, one on each side of it. The clusters seemed to correspond to the margins of the large magnetic anomalies created by the iron rods.

Yves Rocard proposed one possible explanation for effects of this kind.[7] He suggested that dowsers only respond to small magnetic gradients – up to 100 nanoteslas per metre or so – that are found in nature. When dowsers walk through much larger magnetic gradients, such as those directly above the iron rods, they no longer respond. This idea is consistent with the supersensory explanation of dowsing success: like those of

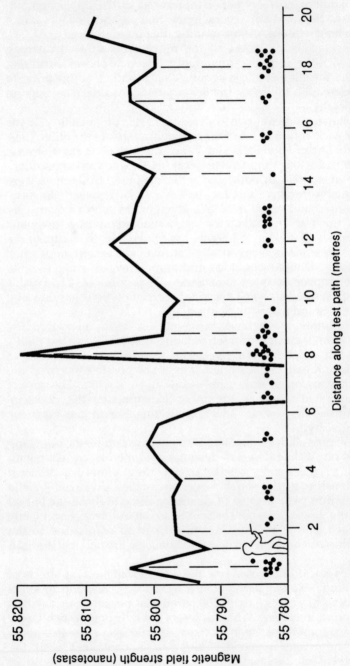

Fig.4 Investigators at Utah State University found that dowsers' responses correlated with small magnetic field changes

whales and pigeons, the brains of humn beings could be programmed to respond to natural magnetic cues for use in navigation but to ignore unnaturally large magnetic changes.

Alternatively, there may be a simpler explanation. Having responded to the field change at the beginning of a large magnetic anomaly, walking dowsers may have a 'dead time' of a few seconds, during which they cannot respond at all. By the time they are ready to respond again, they may have walked right through the anomaly.

Whatever the reason for this particular effect, the Utah State University experiments showed that when they walked across suitable magnetic landscapes dowsers' responses *did* correlate with small magnetic changes, as predicted by the supersensory explanation of dowsing success. What the results did not show, however, was that this could actually help a dowser to achieve good results in the field. Evidence bearing on this last point came from a study carried out in 1982 by the Institute for Natural Geography and Technical Geology at the University of Lund in Sweden.[8]

As in the American dowsing experiments, dowsers walked one by one along various test courses or through test areas. The test site in the island of Gotland was underlain by karst terrane where underground water flowed along solution channels in limestone – a situation in which Hans Schröter and a few other dowsers have produced impressive results. There were apparently no surface cues to guide the dowsers.

In each experiment the investigators first measured the positions of the dowsers' rod movements and then conducted geophysical surveys to locate the channels. Generally, the dowsers' rod movements tended to cluster above the geophysically located channels. In one test of twenty dowsers, in addition to carrying out electromagnetic and ground radar surveys, the scientists measured small changes in the intensity of the Earth's magnetic field, as Duane Chadwick had done. The measurements indicated a small magnetic trough, 25 nanoteslas deep, right over one of the channels. The dowsers' rod movements clustered together in the magnetic trough.

The University of Lund study therefore showed that dowsers sometimes move their rods at places where the Earth's magnetism changes slightly, thereby achieving success. But, as in the Utah State University investigation, the dowsers' subconscious minds could have received other sensory information as well as magnetic data. So the tests did not prove beyond doubt that the dowsers were using their magnetic supersense. To demonstrate that, we would need experiments showing that, when screened from conventional sensory cues, dowsers' rod movements still correlate with small magnetic changes.

As we saw in chapter five, the Munich group of scientists devised ingenious tests of precisely the required kind – plank experiments. Yet disappointingly, despite all the money and talent available, the scientists did not specifically test the claim that some dowsers' responses are caused by small magnetic changes.

Fortunately though, the German scientists did carry out a few plank experiments to test dowsers' response to *large* magnetic anomalies.[9] Investigators placed the plank in such a way that blindfolded and disorientated dowsers walked through a large magnetic feature produced by a buried magnet in the soil. In one such instance, dowsers walked along the plank through a gigantic anomaly, the vertical component of the Earth's magnetic field (measured at ground level) increasing from its normal local level of about 43,000 nanoteslas to a peak of about 48,000 nanoteslas. The magnetic disturbance extended for one or two metres on either side of the magnetic peak.

If the dowsers were to respond to this steep magnetic feature in the same way that the students at Utah State University had apparently responded to similar large anomalies, we would expect their rod movements to cluster near the margins of the big magnetic anomaly. What happened was precisely that. The dowsers' rods did not move at the magnetic peak itself, but one or two metres on either side of it. This result was therefore consistent with the American and Swedish findings, supporting the concept that, like whales and pigeons, dowsers can unconsciously respond to small magnetic changes.

The German investigators came up with other evidence that some dowsers make use of a magnetic supersense. In 1962 Yves Rocard had claimed that dowsers could detect the small magnetic effects caused by an electric current flowing through a wire coil. The Munich group of scientists developed Rocard's pioneering experimental approach into a powerful double-blind protocol capable of yielding unambiguous results.[10]

In Rocard's simple tests, dowsers had walked through a large wire coil connected via an on-and-off switch to a 6 volt battery. By varying the resistance in the circuit, Rocard had been able to alter the current flowing through the coil and therefore the intensity of the magnetic field. In their more sophisticated experiments, the German investigators attached a small vertical wire coil at shoulder level to a wooden post and connected it up to a signal generator producing between one and a thousand current pulses per second. The current gave a maximum field of less than 500 nanoteslas at the centre of the coil. The current and

Andrew Williamson (the author's father), based in northern Tanzania, carried out both dowsing and geophysical (earth resistivity) surveys for clients

Andrew Williamson pinpointing a borehole site for water in the crystalline rocks of Kenya

Pump testing of a hole sited by Andrew Williamson on volcanic lavas near the great volcano Kilimanjaro in northern Tanzania. This hole yielded more than 600 litres of water per minute

John Mullins, a Wiltshire mason and professional dowser, whose remarkable water-finding feats throughout the British Isles intrigued scientists of the Victorian period

its associated magnetic field were switched on and off at random by a computer, enabling the tests to be conducted in full double-blind mode.

The German investigators asked dowsers to walk past the coil and show a dowsing response if they thought the field was switched on. Before being tested, the dowsers were allowed 20-minute training periods during which they could walk through fields of various frequencies and intensities, choosing the combination that seemed to suit them best.

Seventy-six dowsers took part in the experiments, each dowser participating in several series of tests. Although about a dozen dowsers turned in significantly above-chance results in their first series of tests, taking all the dowsers together, the results were no better than chance.

One of the 76 dowsers did, however, perform exceptionally well. Of course, with a group as large as this, by chance alone we would expect one or two dowsers to turn in good performances. But if magnetism has nothing to do with dowsing ability, we would expect the top performers in the magnetic tests to be randomly selected from the group of 76.

The actual results confounded this expectation. For the best performer in the magnetic tests turned out to be none other than Hans Schröter, the most highly regarded dowser in the whole group. In one day of testing, Schröter produced results that would only occur by chance on two out of a hundred occasions, a performance not approached by any other dowser. Although his results were not so good on a second day, the fact remained that the best field dowser turned in the best magnetic performance, implying that magnetism does have something to do with dowsing ability.

But if dowsers do have a magnetic supersense, why did most of the other dowsers perform poorly in the German magnetic experiments? In fact, such a performance is quite consistent with the notion that dowsers can respond to *natural* magnetic cues. Walking through a pulsing magnetic field, up to 500 nanoteslas in strength, is not the same thing at all as crossing a natural magnetic bump of the kind that animals and humans seem to use in navigation. Moreover, in the German tests, the dowsers not only had to involve their conscious minds (in asking themselves the question: is the field on or off?), they also had to produce a conditioned response to the field maximum as they passed the coil. Under natural conditions, as we have seen, dowsers crossing large magnetic features of this kind seem to produce two responses, one before and one after the magnetic peak. The unavoidably boring, repetitive nature of the experiments could have been another factor likely to prevent the dowsers from achieving good test results, and could account for the decline in some dowsers' performance in their second and subsequent series of tests.

Bearing all these points in mind, it is perhaps surprising that Hans Schröter was able to do as well as he did. It may be that the engineer owed his success not to any greater magnetic sensitivity than the other dowsers, but rather to his superior ability to adapt his responses to the artificial magnetic conditions of the experiments. The capacity to develop conditioned responses to appropriate magnetic or other supersensory cues may be a critical factor in the make-up of a successful dowser.

So, taken together, the results of the American, Swedish and German dowsing investigations agree with the predictions of the supersensory theory of dowsing – at least as far as magnetism is concerned. They suggest that all dowsers unconsciously respond to the natural magnetic cues that whales and other animals use in navigation. Moreover, a few outstanding dowsers like Hans Schröter seem to be able to obtain conditioned responses to complex artificial magnetic pulses produced in the laboratory.

But what about other supersenses? The essence of the supersensory explanation of dowsing success is that dowsers can respond to several geophysical signals, good ones being able to select the most relevant cues available. If the theory is right, dowsers should also make use of other supersensory cues – for instance earth vibrations (microseisms). In chapter seven, we saw how, in principle, these vibrations could let a dowser detect hidden faults and fractures.

Until recently, there was no solid evidence whatsoever to support the notion of a human supersensitivity to earth vibrations. That situation changed completely in 1989 when the Munich group of scientists came up with some remarkable findings that lend credence to the idea.[11]

Recall that in chapter five we saw how some of the dowsers being tested by the German scientists achieved excellent results at a test site in the valley of the River Sinn, north of Rieneck in Bavaria. Hans Schröter had there chosen a site for a well on valley alluvium immediately above a concealed fault. Despite being blindfolded and subjected to stringent experimental controls, three dowsers moved their rods within a few metres of Hans Schröter's well position.

Could a snake-like supersensitivity to earth vibrations explain these remarkable results? In chapter seven we saw how alluvial sediments might be expected to amplify the earth vibrations above a hidden fault to give a narrow band of enhanced microseismicity on the surface. The concept could therefore explain not only how Hans Schröter selected the site in the first place, but also how the other dowsers were independently able to locate the same position.

To test the idea, after the dowsing experiments the German scientists measured earth vibrations around Hans Schröter's site. The findings were most intriguing. There was significant microseismicity in the area, with the amplitudes of the vibrations peaking at an infrasonic frequency just below 20 hertz. At the well site itself, the vertical components of the vibration velocities (the most convenient parameters to measure) were significantly larger than at points 2 metres away, while those 4 metres away from the dowser's site were smaller still.

To see if this effect was a persistent one, the scientists repeated the measurements early in the following morning, when vibrations due to road traffic should have been less intense. As expected, the vibrations around Hans Schröter's site were smaller than before. But the scientists found exactly the same effect: vibrations at the dowser's site itself were larger than those 4 metres away.

Unfortunately, the scientists did not make enough measurements to be absolutely certain that the microseismic anomaly was linked with the concealed fault system. Nevertheless, the German scientists' work does provide a solid foundation for the idea that some dowsers can sense the narrow bands of intensified earth vibrations above certain geological faults.

So already there is experimental support for the general notion that successful dowsers may use at least two supersenses – magnetism and earth vibrations – to help locate faults, fracture zones and other geological structures. How could these ideas work out in detail?

We saw in chapter eight how faults often produce long magnetic anomalies of a kind that whales and other animals may use in navigation. These anomalies, which we can think of as ridges or cliffs running across the magnetic landscape, arise for various reasons. For example, the rocks on one side of the fault may contain more magnetite or other magnetic minerals than the rocks on the other side or circulating groundwater may have deposited magnetic iron minerals along the fault plane.

Indeed, most mineral veins are mineralized faults, the lode typically containing much larger quantities of magnetite or other magnetic minerals than the surrounding rocks. These lodes therefore produce sharp ridges crossing the magnetic land-scape, easily detectable by magnetically sensitive dowsers. As the breadth of the magnetic ridge roughly corresponds to the width of the mineral vein causing it, skilled dowsers should be able to determine the width of a mineral lode hidden beneath the soil. Remember William Cookworthy's claim that a good Cornish dowser could discover all the geometrical properties of concealed lodes, including their changes in breadth, where they pinched out to nothing, and where they were displaced by cross-cutting fractures.

While individual mineral veins produce localized magnetic anomalies, major faults may be accompanied by much larger magnetic features. Typically, a dowser walking towards such a fault might detect an increase in magnetic slope 50 to 100 metres before reaching it. The actual fault line itself might produce a smaller magnetic feature, standing up as a narrow central spine on top of a broad magnetic ridge. So the dowser could experience a second response when crossing the fault line itself.

Russian geologists have reported several examples of this phenomenon – dowsers seeming to sense the presence of a fault before actually coming to it. This brings to mind the account in Chapter Two of how a dowser, being led blindfolded over Greenhow Hill in Yorkshire, suddenly exclaimed, 'Ah'm comin' to summat.' Soon afterwards he crossed the line of the North Craven Fault, and his hazel rod twisted so violently that the point hit his chest.

At the point where the dowser had apparently detected it, the North Craven Fault took the form of a shattered belt of rock a few metres wide. Like many other faults and fracture zones, it would have been acting as a channel for flowing groundwater. So could a skilfully deployed magnetic supersense explain successful dowsing for water as well as for minerals?

In many water-finding situations a dowser would certainly find a sense of magnetism useful. This is particularly so in the case of the crystalline rocks typical of the mining areas where mineral dowsers first discovered that they could find water.

Professor Gene Simmons, a geophysicist at the Massachusetts Institute of Technology, has reported an excellent example of how a magnetic supersense could have helped dowsers achieve success in these conditions.[12] Local dowsers had chosen sites for two water wells in crystalline rocks near Boston, Massachusetts. As in other regions where crystalline rocks occur, large supplies of water were difficult to find: most wells in this part of New England yielding only eight to twelve litres of water per minute. Yet pumping tests had shown that these two dowsed wells, about 600 metres deep, yielded *1500 to 1900 litres of water per minute*.

To discover why the dowsers had been so successful,

Simmons conducted gravity and magnetic surveys in the vicinity of the wells. He found that the dowsers had sited the wells within a linear magnetic anomaly only a few metres wide. The steep magnetic feature marked the site of a north-east-trending fracture zone that was channelling the flow of groundwater – hence the exceptionally high yields of the wells.

Several other high-yield water wells in the crystalline rocks of New England are located in similar fracture zones. In an address to the American Society of Dowsers, Simmons mentioned two examples: wells for a nuclear power station at Seabrook, New Hampshire and wells for an industrial plant in Attleboro, Massachusetts, owned by the Texas Instruments business corporation. These fracture zones were located by geologists, working from aerial photographs, but presumably could also have been found by magnetically sensitive dowsers.

Apart from New England, there are many other regions throughout the world underlain by impermeable, crystalline rocks where large supplies of water are difficult to find unless the water finder – traditionally a dowser – can locate suitable faults or fracture zones. As we have seen, the crystalline rocks of Sri Lanka is one area where Hans Schröter has recently found water with spectacular success.

Another such region of crystalline rocks lies in Brittany, France, where local people have for generations relied on dowsers to find suitable sites for wells. Many of these dowsed locations have yielded excellent supplies of valuable water. For instance, a dowser reportedly located a water-bearing fissure near the town of Ploërmel in Brittany that later yielded 600 litres per minute of mineral water for the Katell Roc company.[13] In East Africa, too, dowsers have sometimes managed to find huge water supplies in fractured zones of ancient crystalline rock. My father sited such a well, 100 metres deep, near Mombo, Tanzania, that yielded more than 800 litres of water per minute.[14]

Apart from faults and fracture zones, there is another class of water-bearing structures that magnetically sensitive dowsers could detect even more reliably – volcanic dykes. These old feeder channels for volcanoes, usually packed with small magnetite crystals, sometimes act as impermeable barriers that guide groundwater flow in such a way that a well drilled to one side of a dyke may yield a good supply of water, while one drilled the other side yields none at all. More to the point, because the minerals they contain decompose easily, some volcanic dykes are themselves superb water-bearers, particularly when they occur in impermeable rocks such as granite.

But not all water-bearing faults, fracture zones or other

structures give rise to magnetic ridges of the kind a dowser might detect with a magnetic supersense. If the magnetic properties of the rocks on either side of the fault are the same, there may be no magnetic anomaly. The fault in the Sinn valley, Bavaria, that was detected by Hans Schröter and other dowsers seems to have been one of this kind.

In such instances, good dowsers may still be able to locate the fault in question – by means of their supersensitivity to earth vibrations. Apart from the Sinn valley fault, another possible fault that might have signalled its presence in this way was the one apparently detected by John Mullins near Waterford, Ireland in 1887, when he located a spectacularly successful well for a local firm of bacon curers. Mullins sited his well on a deposit of glacial clays and gravels, which lay over the suspected fault – just the situation where a band of enhanced earth vibrations could be expected. The energizing source could have been heavy seas breaking against the western coast of Ireland or even factories and traffic in the nearby town of Waterford.

Another class of water-bearing structures not generally associated with magnetic anomalies are fissures in basalt volanic lavas. As we have seen, Major Pogson and several other dowsers have shown a remarkable ability to detect such fissures. Could they have done so by exploiting their supersensitivity to Earth vibrations?

Further scientific investigations would obviously be needed to confirm this idea. Even more ambitious studies would be required to find out if, as seems likely, successful dowsers make use not only of magnetism and earth vibrations, but also other Sphinx-like supersenses. But whatever the outcome of such future work, it is clear that the supersensory theory is already strong enough to explain much of the ancient mystery of dowsing – how certain dowsers can detect the hidden faults, fracture zones and other structures that are associated with mineral veins, flowing groundwater or radon.

If dowsers can use their supersenses to detect fracture zones, perhaps the supersensory theory could also explain some twentieth-century oil dowsing feats. Although oil and gas are often found in structural fold traps in sandstone, sometimes these hydrocarbons are trapped in fracture zones, particularly in limestone. For instance, in the Trenton-Black River limestone formation in the Michigan Basin of North America, oil is often found occupying fracture zones in the very dense limestone. Some of these fracture zones have been enlarged by the passage of corrosive magnesium-rich fluids into veritable caverns that can trap large quantities of oil.

These zones have proved difficult to locate by conventional methods, and geologists have had to resort to sophisticated geochemical techniques to find them, such as the measurement of helium anomalies in soil (like radon, helium gas rises along faults and fractures). But recently Richard Barca, a local oil exploration geologist, has found that certain dowsers can be helpful in this situation, one in particular being apparently able to pinpoint potentially oil-bearing fracture zones with remarkable accuracy.[15] If confirmed, such feats might also be explained by a supersensitivity to fault-linked influences such as changes in magnetism or earth vibrations.

The supersensory concept's explanatory power is not restricted to dowsers' apparent detection of faults, fracture zones and dykes. We may recall that the Russian geologists claimed success not only in locating such features, and the minerals and water associated with them, but also other geological structures. For instance, they used dowsing to delineate the boundaries of massive sulphide ore bodies that are mined for copper, zinc, lead and other metals as well as the chromite ore bodies that are sources of chromium metal. A magnetic supersense could explain these claims – sulphide ore bodies typically contain the magnetic iron sulphide mineral pyrrhotite while chromite is also magnetic.

Human sensitivity to magnetism could also account for the Russian geologists' claim that dowsers could trace the outlines of hidden diamond pipes. Such pipes are actually the conduits of ancient volcanoes, and although diamonds themselves are not magnetic, the volcanic matrix containing them does contain magnetite and other magnetic minerals of the spinel family. Eroded diamond pipes therefore produce magnetic features that could easily be traced by a dowser who had learned to use his or her magnetic supersense.

Yet another surprising opportunity for a magnetically sensitive dowser lies in the search for alluvial gold. Although gold itself is not magnetic, gold particles are sometimes concentrated together with magnetite in certain gravel deposits, which therefore produce magnetic anomalies. Russian geologists have indeed used dowsing to locate gold deposits of this kind.[16]

Could the skilful deployment of a magnetic supersense also explain dowsers' apparent uncanny ability to locate old foundations, ditches, graves, tunnels and the like? All such features produce small magnetic anomalies for the following reasons. Soil contains the red iron oxide mineral haematite, which only picks up a little magnetism in the Earth's magnetic field. But processes taking place in the soil's topmost layer, such as burning and fermentation slowly convert the haematite there to the more magnetizable minerals magnetite and maghemite. As a result, the top layer of soil generally picks up more magnetism from the Earth's field than the layers beneath. So wherever people have disturbed the layering by digging holes or ditches, or have replaced the soil with less magnetic materials such as stone in old foundations or air in tunnels, they have at the same time produced magnetic anomalies.[17]

Exploiting these magnetic properties of soils, archaeologists now often carry out magnetic surveys using proton magnetometers before starting their spadework. Like the caesium vapour instruments used by Duane Chadwick at Utah State University, proton magnetometers are very sensitive devices that measure the total strength of the Earth's magnetic field. The archaeologist passes the magnetometer's sensor systematically over the site of interest, the readings may be electronically processed to generate maps of the local magnetic topography.

Magnetic maps of this kind sometimes give startling pictures of hidden ditches, walls, tunnels and graves – the very features that some dowsers have apparently located with eerie accuracy. Remember how, despite being blindfolded and having to perform before the assembled *haut monde* of Paris, Barthelemy Bléton in 1782 reportedly traced the twists and turns of an aqueduct running beneath the Jardins de Luxembourg with uncanny precision. Other dowsers, including the American, Louis Matacia and the Russian, Alexander Pluzhnikov have also impressive records in detecting underground tunnels. Could these dowsers have been relying on their magnetic supersense?

At first sight this idea looks very attractive. But there are several difficulties. We saw in chapter eight that if we do have magnetic sense organs, they are likely to be in our heads. Walking dowsers would therefore detect magnetic changes at head level rather than at the ground itself. In traditional dowsing this would create no problems, for the magnetic anomalies produced by geological faults and other structures extend far above the Earth's surface. Underground tunnels, too, usually create magnetic anomalies that persist well above ground level. But shallow archaeological features such as graves give rise to shallow anomalies that decay rapidly with increasing height above the ground. For this reason, when carrying out magnetic surveys, archaeologists keep the magnetometer's sensor as close to the ground as possible. Since dowsers do not normally crawl around with their heads to the ground, their ability to detect the magnetic signals produced by shallow archaeological features must be somewhat limited.

There are other reasons why a magnetic supersense cannot

explain all archaeological dowsers' successes. Several of Denis Briggs' successes in locating old church foundations, for example, were achieved inside buildings where large magnetic variations might be expected to obliterate the weak signals due to the buried features. At the moment, therefore, it seems that while possibly accounting for the apparent detection by dowsers of features such as tunnels and deep foundations, the rôle of a magnetic supersense in archaeological dowsing may be somewhat restricted.

So, if magnetism is not the whole answer, could a sensitivity to earth vibrations have played a part in achievements such as those of Denis Briggs? The idea certainly seems feasible: the intensity of microseisms might vary considerably with the nature of the material just below the surface and could be picked up by the dowser's feet. Further investigations are badly needed.

So as well as explaining the well-attested ability of dowsers to locate faults, fracture zones, and to a lesser extent other geological structures, the supersensory theory now seems all set to make sense of some at least of the archaeological dowsers' claims. How the theory works out in detail will be a matter for future research to decide. It may be that the rôle of the supersenses – and conventional senses – in dowsing varies widely between different dowsers and different dowsing situations.

In water dowsing, for instance, good dowsers like Hans Schröter probably rely on their knowledge of local groundwater conditions and visual hints to select suitable general areas for drilling. But when they need to locate precise water-bearing fissures or fracture zones, they may go into supersensory mode. At the Sinn valley site in Bavaria, Schröter may have used earth vibrations to locate the concealed fault, while perhaps using his magnetic supersense when locating water-bearing fissures in crystalline rock in Sri Lanka and elsewhere.

For dowsers looking for mineral lodes in a known mining area, or archaeological remains at an existing site, the position is somewhat different. The dowsers already know where to start searching and may go directly into supersensory mode, perhaps generally using magnetic cues to pinpoint the exact positions of their underground targets. But even at this stage, dowsers may also use visual cues if they are available – we have seen how, when dowsing for old church foundations in the north of England, Denis Briggs seems to have been guided by tell-tale features in existing buildings.

This provisional model of how good dowsers achieve success needs to be tested by further high-quality research aimed at finding out which supersensory cues particular dowsers use in particular situations. Using the experimental methods and protocols developed by the Munich group, further plank experiments could be performed in a variety of geological and archaeological situations. The results could be compared with the findings of subsequent geophysical surveys, using magnetometers, seismometers and other instruments.

To carry out such work, co-operation between physicists, psychologists, biologists and Earth scientists is essential. Hitherto Earth scientists have tended to remain aloof from dowsing research – no geologists participated in the Munich project – but there are signs that this attitude is changing. In 1992 Professor Hans-Dieter Betz spoke on dowsing research at the annual convention of the German Geophysical Society and was preparing a discussion meeting with senior Earth scientists on the subject.

Concurrently with pure research of this kind, scientifically based learning methods could be developed to improve dowsers' use of supersensory cues. Although progress may be slow at first, there is one good reason to believe that it will be ultimately successful – the amazing flexibility of the human brain. If blind people can learn to see with their ears, as in facial vision, there is no reason why dowsers cannot learn to use their hidden supersenses much more efficiently.

Such research programmes are likely to take some years to bear fruit. In the meantime, our provisional model of dowsing success suggests that those of us who dowse as a hobby rather than in a professional capacity could do much to improve our performance. It certainly needs improving – the performance of the vast majority of dowsers today can only be described as abysmal.

Having learned to obtain dowsing responses with the V-rod or angle rods, what should our next steps be? First, we need to adopt a modest, cautious approach to our dowsing activities. Many novice dowsers, swept away by enthusiasm for the magical technique they think they have discovered, believe they can find anything anywhere. Yet, as our survey has shown, such over-confidence is misplaced. The flipping of a rod in our hands means little in itself, we have to train our unconscious minds to flip the rod in response to appropriate supersensory cues in suitable contexts.

To do this, we obviously need repeated practice in places where such cues are available. William Cookworthy advised young dowsers to gain experience by dowsing over known mineral lodes and his advice could hardly be bettered today. Along several stretches of the Cornish coast – near Land's End for example, you can see mineral lodes, cutting through granite or slate, exposed on the foreshore and these make excellent targets for dowsing practice. Cookworthy's diagram (see illustration section) shows a good way of doing this: walk in a zig-zag fashion so that you repeatedly cross the margins of the lode.

Having trained oneself to obtain dowsing responses at the margins of visible mineral lodes, the next step is to try to trace lodes that are hidden by beach deposits or soil, using exactly the same method as before. Use pegs or other markers to indicate the margins of the lode.

While mineral lodes – in other words mineralized faults – may be accessible to dowsers living near mining areas, many of them have now been worked out and many beginners will prefer the more common, unmineralized faults as alternative targets for dowsing practice. You can find out information about faults in your area from local geological maps (in the Uni ʾ Kingdom obtainable from the British Geological Survey, Ke〉 ʾrth – see address at end of book).

Like lodes, you can often see faults exposed in clif, long the coastline, and it is intriguing to try and follow tɬ ʾ course inland from the cliff tops or along the beach. The bes; faults to practise on are those that abruptly bring together two different kinds of rock – shale and sandstone for example. As in the case of mineral lodes, once you've learned to trace visible faults, you can then try your hand at tracing concealed ones.

When searching for hidden mineral lodes or faults, many dowsers, including myself, experience recurrent rod movements at regular intervals. William Cookworthy commented on these rhythmic movements 'every three, four or five yards', but advised beginners to ignore them. Later dowsers, heedless of Cookworthy's advice, have propounded elaborate, sometimes convoluted, theories to explain these repetitive responses. Some have invoked complex interference patterns of electromagnetic waves, others have spoken of 'global energy grids'. It is far more likely that these regular rod movements are caused by rhythms related to the dowser's walk (for instance changes in muscle tension) and have nothing to do with the external environment.

Assuming we have trained our unconscious supersenses to detect hidden faults and fractures, how can we apply this ability to water-finding? There is no simple way of becoming a good water dowser today. Faults and fractures are not always the best places to site wells. With increasing concern about depletion and pollution of groundwater supplies, integrated groundwater resource management is essential and new water wells or boreholes must be sited with the greatest care. Expertise is required in the complex subject of hydrogeology and other fields so that an inexperienced dowser working alone is unlikely to produce the best result. Would-be water dowsers will contribute most if they co-operate with other specialists such as hydrogeologists and planners.

Local dowsers in Kibwezi, Kenya, have recently helped their communities to find much-needed water supplies in just this way.[18] Much of this area is underlain by crystalline rock where water is difficult to find unless the borehole or well intersects a fault or fracture zone. The local dowsers found that their dowsed sites correlated well with those selected by experts using geophysical fault-finding instruments and that wells dug there were generally successful. Having validated their technique in this way, the local water dowsers were later able to work successfully without geophysical assistance.

The success of this project shows that in certain geological situations not only experts like Hans Schröter but also quite inexperienced dowsers can sometimes perform useful work. Such conditions exist in places in the British Isles – for instance in the granitic Isles of Scilly – and it is not surprising that local dowsers, such as Donovan Wilkins, the star of a 1989 BBC TV series on dowsing, have come up with some spectacular successes there. But such situations are not all that common; many areas of Britain and elsewhere are underlain by permeable sedimentary rocks. Here, water flows through the pore spaces of the rock and the best sites for wells do not necessarily lie over faults or fissures. In such regions, dowsers who believe – as most still do – that all underground water flows in 'water veins' may well do more harm than good. Such dowsers often locate wells in most unsuitable places in the erroneous belief that a 'water vein' lies below.

Generally speaking, therefore, a beginner at dowsing seeking to develop his or her latent supersensory abilities might be advised to avoid water finding, with all its complexity and pitfalls. As ideal targets such as mineral lodes or geological faults are not always accessible, why not try your hand at tracing more familiar underground features – water and gas pipes, cables, sewers and archaeological remains? First practise over known features, training yourself to respond as you pass over the pipe or whatever. Once you've learned to do this, you could try tracing unknown features of the same kind, walking in zigzag fashion and marking the positions of your responses with pegs or other suitable markers.

How can you verify your findings? One way, as we have seen, is by digging. But excavation may not be feasible and is in any case expensive and time consuming. Archaeologists are increasingly using magnetometers and other remote sensing equipment to survey sites as an alternative to excavation and this offers a splendid opportunity for dowsers to have their results checked. As a result of Professor Richard Bailey's work with Denis Briggs, many professional archaeologists in Britain are now willing to accept help from dowsers, provided they approach their subject rationally and are suitably modest about their own capabilities. Dowsers who say they can divine the depth, nature or even the age of what lies underground will get short shrift from most archaeologists. The magnetite crystals recently discovered in our brains may respond to tiny magnetic field changes produced by things underground but they cannot give us miraculous psychic powers.

Part Two

Author dowsing with V-rod on the Dorset coast. A geological fault can be seen in the cliffs behind

A dowsing response

Hans Schröter dowsing with angle rods in one of the double-blind experiments conducted by the Munich group of scientists. Walking on the top floor of a two-storey barn, he is trying to locate an artificial dowsing target on the ground floor below him

11   Earth Energies

Until the recent growth of environmental consciousness, most Westerners regarded the Earth as little more than a storehouse of useful things to be exploited as quickly as possible. We valued mountains for their mineral potential, trees for their wood, and pumped water and oil out of the ground with little thought for the environmental problems that we were bequeathing to future generations. Traditional dowsing, focusing as it did on the search for minerals and water, was very much part of this milieu.

In the last twenty years or so, though, some dowsers have made claims more in line with the attitudes of those ancient peoples who seem to have had a greater respect for the Earth. Thus, in Britain, such dowsers obtain responses at places prehistoric people held sacred – certain springs and wells or sites of stone circles, henges and barrows.

Such activities may have been originally inspired by the belief that holy wells and other ancient sacred sites were always above 'water veins' or 'underground streams'. Later, dowsers were influenced by the claim of Alfred Watkins, a Herefordshire businessman and local worthy, that certain English prehistoric sites are aligned along what he called ley lines.[1, 2] Excited by this idea, some dowsers now say that they can find these ley lines with their dowsing rods. Believing that the alignments emit 'Earth energies' which they can detect, the dowsers often describe them as 'dowsable Earth energy lines'. Some dowsers relate their concept of Earth energies to apparently similar notions developed by non-Western and ancient cultures. Some even believe that the ancient megalith builders of Europe understood these secret underground forces and constructed monuments like Stonehenge to tap them.[3, 4]

Orthodox archaeologists and other scientists have doused these New Age ideas with even more bucketfuls of scorn than those they poured on the old-fashioned mineral and water dowsers' claims. But, remembering how often orthodoxy has been proved wrong in the past, can we be so sure that our self-proclaimed intellectual guardians are right this time?

Certainly, the scientists are right to say that we cannot accept the concept of dowsable Earth energies at face value. To do so would be an insult to those intelligent and hard-working dowsing researchers who have formulated testable ideas and painstakingly carried out controlled experiments. For, despite their sincerity, proponents of dowsable Earth energies have never even managed to present their ideas clearly enough to be tested.

Nevertheless, it would be unwise to dismiss the concept and its surrounding matrix of ideas in a knee-jerk fashion. The disastrous consequences of our present profit-motivated attitude to the Earth are now obvious to most well-informed people. To avert catastrophe, we need not only short-term technological palliatives, such as action to reduce greenhouse gas emissions, but also long-term shifts in attitude towards the Earth. We need to look at all alternative points of view, including those embodied in the traditions of non-Western and early European cultures. In their concept of Earth energy, could the dowsers and their New Age camp followers have intuitively stumbled upon truths that scientists, cocooned within their narrow specialities, have overlooked?

It is true that many cultures held surprisingly similar beliefs concerning sacred places where people could draw healing or life-sustaining powers from the Earth. Springs were obviously life-giving, and were often associated not only with fertilization and healing, but also with the gifts of insight and prophecy. In Norse mythology, two holy springs, one the source of all wisdom and the other the spring of fate, lay beneath one root of Yggdrasil, the world ash tree. To be permitted to drink from the well of wisdom, the god Odin was willing to sacrifice one of his eyes.

The Greeks, too, accredited many sacred springs with powers of healing, wisdom and prophecy. At the Delphic oracle, originally sacred to Gaia (Mother Earth), the prophetess would first drink from the spring water. Then she would mount a tripod over the fissure, inhale its fumes until she entered a trance and then mumble her prophecies. At Clarus, near Colophon, sacred to the wise god Apollo, the seer would drink the water from a holy well and then pronounce the oracle in verse. At another oracle, sacred to Demeter, the gentle goddess of the cornfield, priestesses would prophesy after lowering a mirror into the well by rope.[5]

In Britain, the Romans dedicated the renowned springs at Bath to Minerva, goddess of wisdom. Before the Roman conquest, the springs were sacred to the Celtic goddess Sulis, and before that perhaps to Minerva's ancestress, the Great

Goddess, who seems to have been universally worshipped by Europeans in Neolithic and Early Bronze Age times.

As well as springs, ancient and non-Western peoples revered many other natural sites. Aboriginal tribes in Australia held many places sacred – certain rock outcrops, hills, caves and trees. By performing suitable rituals at these 'sites of the Dreamtime', some tribes believed they could release a mist-like essence called *kurunba* that would fertilize and promote the growth of nearby plants and animals. At one sacred boulder, after performing the appropriate ritual a tribal elder would break flakes off the rock, thereby releasing the *kurunba* contained in it.[6]

The Indian tribes of North America also believed certain mountains, and other places to be holy. Some tribes, too, held that a life essence flowed through the Earth and its cargo of living things. The Pueblo Indians' name for this force was *Po-wa-ha* (water-wind-breath).

But it was the Chinese, with their literary culture and capacity for abstract thought, who developed ideas of this kind to their furthest extent. As the 'Earth Mysteries' writer, Paul Devereux, has pointed out, the name for the Chinese system of geomancy, *Feng Shui* (literally wind and water) closely resembles the 'water-wind-breath' of the Pueblo Indians and indeed the Chinese notion, though far more complicated, in many respects resembles the ideas of the native Americans and Australians.

Feng Shui has been described as the acupuncture of the Earth, for the Chinese not only studied the flow of what they called *ch'i* (life breath or cosmic breath) through the Earth, they aimed to control it, just as the acupuncturist tries to control the flow of life force through the human body. *Ch'i* flows quickly in mountainous regions but sluggishly in plains, it rushes along straight features such as roads and water courses. If a straight feature of this kind points at the front of a house, it will cause harm unless the flow of *ch'i* can be stopped by, for example, the suitable placing of a pond (water attracts and contains *chi*. As well as Earth and water, the Chinese geomants believed air, too, to be an important channel for *ch'i* – a house exposed to cold, gusting winds would be subject to a harmful form of *ch'i* called *sha*.[7]

But the fact that several ancient and non-western peoples believed in fertilizing, 'water-wind-breath' fluids does not mean that some energy akin to *ch'i* actually flows between ancient sacred sites and dowsers can detect it. To see if there could be any truth at all in such seemingly ludicrous ideas, let us look closely at the claims of one of the most highly regarded Earth energy dowsers – the late Dr J. Havelock Fidler.

After a career as an agricultural research scientist, Dr Fidler settled in the little village of Shieldaig, on the northern coast of the rugged Applecross peninsula in north-west Scotland. Fidler became interested in Earth energies after reading a book by the dowser Guy Underwood who claimed that he could detect and identify a weird variety of ley lines linking sacred sites.[8] Underwood had used a special, home-made dowsing tool, built around a tensed strip of copper, which he called an oasis rod. Fidler constructed a similar rod for himself and spent many days in the local Applecross mountains, searching for what he thought were Earth energy lines running between what he took to be cairns or single standing stones. Finally, he drew up a map showing his findings which he published in a book that has been widely read by people interested in Earth Mysteries.[9]

On first inspecting Fidler's map of Earth energy lines in the Applecross peninsula, I was inclined to dismiss the whole thing as nonsense. One could not even be sure that Fidler's standing stones had been placed there by humans, in view of the numerous similar boulders left behind by the ice when the glaciers last retreated from this part of Scotland. As for his alleged energy lines, there was no evidence that they were anything other than the products of suggestion acting on an over-heated imagination.

But then I compared Fidler's Earth energy map with a geological map of the Applecross peninsula that showed the positions of the cracks – dykes and faults – where the Earth's crust had broken in response to past pressures and tensions. The result was astonishing. There is a remarkable correspondence between Fidler's energy lines and these ancient cracks in the Earth's crust. While the energy lines do not precisely coincide in position with the cracks, the trends of the two sets of linear features correspond to a surprising degree.

For example, in the ancient Lewisian crystalline rocks exposed near Shieldaig village and another area on the northern coast of the Applecross peninsula, Fidler found closely-spaced energy lines running towards the north-west. This is the precise direction along which large numbers of basic dykes were injected locally when the Earth's crust split apart during a great volcanic outburst in Lewisian times, about 2,000 million years ago. Fidler found another energy line running north-west across the mountains of Torridonian Sandstone in the centre of the peninsula. In the region bordering this line, the Earth's crust split along north-west-trending cracks, along which basalt dykes were injected during another volcanic episode that shook western Scotland about 55 million years ago. The crystalline roots of a great volcano that dominated the region in those days are exposed in the beautiful Cuillin Hills of Skye, about 20 kilometres to the south-west of the Applecross peninsula.

Later on during the same violent period of earthquakes and volcanism, the Earth's crust near the western coast of the peninsula split along a roughly north-south direction and more basalt dykes were injected into the cracks. Here, precisely coinciding with one of the dykes, Fidler found a major north-south energy line, running from a point just north of Applecross village to the north-west tip of the peninsula.

Finally, as a *coup de grâce* the area was shaken by a succession of tremendous earthquakes that were probably connected with the opening of a rift between Scotland and Greenland as this part of the North Atlantic Ocean formed. The region reverberated to shock after shock as the whole south-eastern part of the Applecross peninsula slipped downwards along a great fault that runs north-east from a point on the coast north of Applecross village to the northern coast of the peninsula. From what we have already seen, we might expect that Fidler would have found energy lines close to this position. Indeed he did, finding two energy lines radiating in opposite directions from a standing stone in the centre of the peninsula that correspond closely with the position of the fault.

All this suggests that perhaps the dowsers' energy lines – or some of them at least – really do exist after all, in the form of ancient cracks or faults in the Earth's crust. In fact, Fidler seems to have recognized this himself. On comparing his map of energy lines with local geological maps made by research students, Fidler claimed that in almost every case standing stones had been placed over, or very close to, a geological fault or fissure.

But what exactly are the mysterious forces, apparently linked with geological faults, which Earth energy dowsers like Fidler may have sensed? Could they be the same subtle, fault-linked influences that traditional mineral and water dowsers seem able to detect with their supersenses? To help answer this question, we need first to look at a related 'Earth Mystery' – the nature of those strange events that foretell the sudden movements along faults that we call earthquakes.

Fortunately for us, Professor Helmut Tributsch, a German physical chemist, has made an extensive study of pre-earthquake events.[10] By examining a vast amount of document-ary evidence from the ancient world, Europe, the Americas, China, Japan and elsewhere, Tributsch found consistent evidence of a remarkable set of phenomena, that had been hitherto rejected or ignored by orthodox science.

One such phenomenon was the appearance of clouds or fogs before earthquakes. One of the ancient Egyptian 'Pyramid

Texts' stated that during earthquakes the bones of Akeru, the Earth god, trembled simultaneously with the clouding of the sky and the darkening of the stars. The ancient Greeks also noticed this phenomenon. Aristotle wrote that in clear weather earthquakes were sometimes preceded by a sign: a thin cloud layer, spreading over the sky and darkening the sun.

Much later, in 1799, the great German naturalist, Alexander von Humboldt witnessed a fog of this kind when staying at Cumana, in what is now Venezuela. For several evenings in succession, he noticed that as night fell a red fog rose on the horizon and within a few minutes the whole sky was veiled by cloud. Then, just before the quake, the air felt hot, and black clouds gathered. Finally, two powerful tremors shook the ground and there was a strong electrical discharge (which Humboldt, with remarkable *sang-froid*, monitored on his electroscope).

Humboldt found that the local people of Cumana and other towns in South America had long recognized reddish hazes of this kind as portents of earthquakes. But people in other earthquake-prone parts of the world also knew of such clouds or fogs. Japanese tradition held that before an earthquake a strange air called *chiki* (air from the Earth) comes out of the ground, spreading out to form a fog. Tributsch quoted a typical report in Japanese archives. In 1802, a merchant and a sailor climbed a hill to assess the sailing weather. The sailor was amazed to see the lower slopes of the mountains covered with a strange fog unlike any he had seen before. Remembering the tradition about *chiki* foretelling earthquakes, the merchant decided that the two of them should collect their baggage and leave the inn where they were staying. After they had walked about 15 kilometres, an intense tremor shook the ground. This was the destructive Sado Island earthquake.

Tributsch found another widely believed earthquake omen: water from springs and wells tasted or smelt odd and became murky. Pherecydes of Syros, one of the 'seven wise men' of ancient Greece, is said to have predicted an earthquake three days in advance by the change in appearance, and possibly taste, of water scooped from a spring. Writing in the first century, the Roman naturalist Pliny the Elder mentioned the sudden cloudiness of wells and the repulsive smell of water as a reliable earthquake omen. The same phenomenon was later recorded by the Japanese and, above all, by the Chinese, who, by the 1970s, were using the muddiness and level of water in wells as a successful means of earthquake prediction.

Yet another mysterious phenomenon often reported before earthquakes, Tributsch discovered, was the unusual behaviour of animals. We have already seen some examples: how hibernating snakes come out of the ground, horses become restless, cats and dogs run out of houses. The ancient Greek historian, Diodorus Siculus, recorded an instance of such behaviour as early as 373 BC, when the city of Helice, in the Gulf of Corinth, sank into the sea after a violent earthquake. According to the historian, five days before the quake and to the amazement of the local people, a procession of rats, snakes, weasels, centipedes, worms and beetles left town and set off by road towards the nearby city of Koria.[11]

But of all the unexplained pre-earthquake phenomena that people of different times and cultures have reported, perhaps the most remarkable have been strange lights. European, Japanese and Chinese observers all recorded an astonishing variety of lightforms before or during earthquakes: balls of fire, glowing banners or pillars of light in the sky, and snake-like flames. For example, in AD 450 a fiery sign appeared over Constantinople at the same time as an earthquake shook the city. The Emperor, Senate and clergy promptly took off their shoes and spent several days in prayer.

Perhaps the weirdest of these earthquake lights reported throughout history are the balls of fire. During the earthquake that hit Valparaiso, Chile in 1906, the captain of a ship near the coast saw seven or eight balls of fire rise from a house burning in the hills. The balls moved eastwards and then, one by one, dropped and exploded, detonating as if an artillery bombardment was taking place.

People have seen fire balls of this kind before or during many other earthquakes. For instance, starting on 1 November 1988, witnesses in the Saguenay region of Quebec province, Canada, noticed weird lights in the sky.[12] They saw orange, yellow, white, and green fire balls of various colours repeatedly pop out of the ground. Some people saw fire balls, stationary or moving, hundreds of metres above ground and some saw luminescent droplets of fire fall from the balls. On 23 November, the region was shaken by a quake of 6.5 magnitude that was felt as far away as Washington, DC.

Tributsch believed that these different pre-earthquake phenomena – mysterious clouds, altered taste and smell of water, unusual behaviour of animals, strange lights – were not unrelated, coincidental events, but interlinked Earth processes not yet understood by science. Orthodox western scientists had ignored these phenomena because their reductionist outlook and overspecialization had prevented them from seeing the whole picture.

By contrast, certain ancient and non-Western peoples could

easily accommodate these diverse phenomena within their more holistic world views. Believing that energizing fluids like *ch'i* were always flowing through earth, air, water and living things, they could well understand the pre-earthquake happenings in terms of the altered flow of energy-rich fluids before the Earth itself shook.

The philosophers of ancient Greece elaborated one idea of this kind into a well-thought-out scientific theory. To account for the strange events culminating in earthquakes, the fifth century BC intellectuals, Anaxagoras and Archelaos invoked the concept of *pneuma*, a *ch'i*-like fluid that moved through Earth, water and air. Aristotle developed the notion, conceiving *pneuma* as being like condensed water vapour, but warm and dry rather than wet.[13] He concluded from many observations that before an earthquake, *pneuma* first emerged from the ground, forming characteristic clouds and fogs in the air and darkening the sun. Then, perhaps after a falsely reassuring period of calm, the *pneuma* suddenly flowed back into the Earth, causing it to convulse. After the quake, the *pneuma* escaped completely from the Earth and dispersed.

Now we can begin to see the relevance of all this to the nature of 'dowsable Earth energies'. We have already wondered if these *ch'i*-like energies may be equated with the set of subtle, fault-linked influences – earth vibrations, magnetism, air ionization and so on – that traditional dowsers seem to have used to locate minerals and water. If this is so, then perhaps we could understand the pre-earthquake phenomena – which the ancients attributed to alterations in holistically conceived *ch'i*-like forces – in terms of changes in the same subtle, but apparently dowsable, fault-linked influences.

In doing so, we would naturally have to employ the reductionist mechanisms of modern science. But there is no reason why we should not also continue to value the holistic viewpoints that served ancient and non-western peoples so well. With his concept of Gaia, a living, homoeostatic Earth, the British scientist James Lovelock has constructed a holistic model that nevertheless describes in a reductionist way the slow long-term biological and chemical evolution of the Earth.[14, 15] Perhaps we could try in similar fashion to build an updated and refined understanding of 'dowsable Earth energies' and their pre-earthquake changes that scientists and New Agers might both value.

One of the fault-linked influences we have looked at is air ionization. In chapter nine we saw how the inhalation of positively charged 'small ions' could cause animals and humans to experience the 'serotonin stimulation syndrome' and behave oddly. So if for some reason air ionization increased before quakes, this could perhaps explain some of the reports of strange animal behaviour. Moreover, increased air ionization could possibly explain some of the other mysterious pre-earthquake events. For example, by acting as condensation nuclei for water droplets, airborne ions could also cause the mysterious earthquake fogs that the ancients noticed so often.[16]

But why should the Earth release positively charged ions before earthquakes? The most obvious possible cause is stress – after all earthquakes result when stress build up near a fault plane until rocks slip along it. Moreover, scientists have long known that when some low-symmetry crystals, such as quartz, are squeezed in certain directions, existing negative and positive electric charges within the crystal are separated and current may flow. This is called the piezoelectric effect. Many rocks – granite, gneiss, sandstone and certain volcanic lavas – contain quartz crystals, which are often partially aligned in such a way that when the rock is squeezed, large electrical charges can build up. Repeated, rhythmic squeezing, caused by earthquake waves or even microseisms, could enhance this effect. Such charges could cause ions to form in the air and luminous lightning-like discharges to take place.

So is the piezoelectric effect the driving force behind these strange phenomena? Looking into this question, Helmut Tributsch found that things were not quite so simple. In deserts, where rocks are very dry, the piezoelectric effect may indeed generate luminous discharges and cause air ionization. I myself once witnessed a remarkable lightning-like display from rocky quartzite ridges in southern Morocco, as the sun-heated rocks cooled and contracted in the cold desert night. But in most places the moisture within tiny cracks and pores in the rock lowers the electrical resistance, preventing charges from building up to the point where ionization and luminous phenomena take place.

Tributsch thereupon suggested that the moisture within hairline rock cracks might itself be the key to a remarkable Earth energy conversion process. As stress builds up before a quake, a network of hairline fractures would eat through the rock. The surfaces of these cracks would be coated with moisture, while their interiors would be in partial vacuum. Then, Tributsch argued, a phenomenon called electrochemical glow discharge might take place. Piezoelectric currents, flitting through the rock, would jump across the cracks in the form of high-energy ions, typically positively charged water molecules. Such ions would accelerate across the partial vacuum within a crack, hitting the water molecules lining the opposite side so hard that some would split into high-energy fragments. Each of these fragments would then hit other molecules, generating yet more fragments. The whole process would be a highly efficient means of generating positive ions, which as we have just seen could give rise to the strange fogs or clouds and lead animals to behave oddly.

Moreover, electricity flowing through moist rocks could also explain the pungent odours and strange taste of water from springs or wells and even some of the luminous phenomena before quakes. The currents could cause electrochemical reactions that might liberate gases such as hydrogen, oxygen and chlorine. The first two form an explosive mixture that might produce flames and detonations, while the acrid-smelling chlorine would dissolve in water, giving it an unpleasant taste and odour.

Helmut Tributsch's ingenious electrochemical scheme, which remains hypothetical, is one mechanism whereby rock stress accumulating near a fault plane, might modify and extend any air ionization there due to the upward migration of radon. But there is also evidence that increased stress and other factors operating before earthquakes may directly augment the release of radon from fractures, thereby increasing air ionization by another means. Oversimplifying somewhat, we may therefore conclude that changes in rock stress before earthquakes may cause one of the dowsable, fault-linked influences – air ionization – to alter, thereby playing a part in some of the mysterious pre-earthquake phenomena.

If this is so in the case of one dowsable fault-linked influence, what about others such as earth vibrations and magnetism? It is certainly true that microseismic activity often increases before quakes. We saw in chapter seven how animals such as snakes and scorpions can detect the infrasonic earth tremors that may foretell major earthquakes, while elephants may be able to hear the low-frequency sounds emitted by the trembling ground. So increased earth vibrations before quakes may themselves play a part in causing animals to behave oddly.

What about changes in magnetism and electromagnetism? Theory suggests that alterations in stress before earthquakes should create small magnetic changes. Indeed changes a few nanoteslas in magnitude have been recorded before several earthquakes, for instance the July 1986 North Palm Springs quake in California, caused by movement along the San Andreas fault system.[17] Electromagnetic emissions too, have been monitored before quakes[18] and as we will see shortly it is possible that localized magnetic or electromagnetic events play a part in the formation of the most mysterious of all the pre-earthquake phenomena – light balls.

If dowsers, with their supersenses, can detect fault-linked influences of this kind under normal conditions, could they respond to the changes in these influences before quakes? Some dowsers have claimed precisely that. A missionary in the South American Andes informed Joseph Wüst that by skilled use of their dowsing rods the locals could often predict earthquakes and volcanic eruptions in advance.[19]

More recently, in 1983, Andrei Apostol shocked an assembly of geologists and geophysicists at New York's Lamont-Doherty Geological Observatory by claiming that he had himself success-fully used dowsing to predict earthquakes in Romania. During two periods, August to September 1978 and June to July 1981, Apostol had walked with his dowsing rod at 9 am each day over the inactive Covasna Fault in Transylvania, noting the width of the dowsing zone over the fault. Apostol found that over periods of up to two weeks the width of the dowsing zone would typically first increase slowly and then suddenly decrease. Apostol claimed that these sudden dowsable changes over the Covasna Fault tended to precede deep-focus earthquakes of magnitude 3.0 or larger in the Vrancea seismic zone about 60 kilometres away.[20]

Until other scientists have substantiated these claims, we should treat them with caution. But the notion that dowsers can predict earthquakes is potentially of immense interest, suggest-ing that by using their supersenses certain dowsers can not only detect fault-linked influences themselves, but can also, like animals, respond to the changes in the influences that take place before quakes. Moreover, if Apostol's claims are true, dowsable pre-earthquake changes may take place not only along the active fault involved in the earthquake, but also along old, inactive faults in the same region. This might imply that other strange pre-earthquake phenomena might also occur along inactive faults, possibly heralding later seismic events some distance away.

Let us look at this possibility in relation to those most mysterious of pre-earthquake events – balls of light. Could they be linked with the old, no longer active, faults that good dowsers seem to be able to locate? There are indeed grounds for suspecting a connection. In his *Mineralogia Cornubiensis*,[21] Wil-liam Pryce recommended, as an alternative to dowsing, the observation of 'fiery coruscations' as a means of locating hidden veins of ore:

> Another way of finding veins, which we have heard from those whose veracity we are unwilling to question, is by igneous appearances, or fiery coruscations. The Tinners generally

compare these effluvia to blazing stars, or other whimsical likenesses, as their fears or hopes suggest; and search, with uncommon eagerness, the ground which these jack o'lanthorns have appeared over and pointed out.

One such light ball was reportedly once seen by the owner of a copper mine near Bristol.[22] In 1756 the man told a traveller that he hoped to discover a large copper vein shortly because he had seen a ball of fire 'as big as a man's head' break out of the Earth and shoot up into the sky.

Such reports support the notion that light balls may emerge from the ground not only near active faults before earthquakes, but also in association with inactive, mineralized faults at other times. Paul Devereux and his colleagues have presented a great deal of evidence in favour of this idea.[23]

For example, a remarkable outbreak of mystery lights took place in north-west Wales between December 1904 and July 1905. The episode coincided with a religious revival led by a certain Mary Jones, who seems to have regarded the lights as signs of divine approval for her mission. As a result of their apparent religious significance, the lights aroused great national interest and several London newspapers sent staff to interview Mary Jones and, if possible observe and photograph her lights.

Though at first disappointed, and almost convinced that the lights were imaginary, the *Daily Mail* reporter was startled to see, at about 8.30 pm on the evening of 11 February 1905, a yellow ball of light suddenly appear above the roof of Egryn Chapel, near Barmouth. The light shone with a steady brilliance for over a minute and then suddenly vanished. About 15 minutes later, two new lights appeared, about 30 metres apart, one on either side of the chapel and higher in the sky than the first one. After shining steadily for about 30 seconds, the lights began to flicker 'like a defective arc lamp'. Finally, they steadied again and then flashed out, within a couple of seconds of each other (*Daily Mail*, 13 February, 1905).

Walking southwards along the road to Barmouth later that evening, the same reporter saw other mysterious lights, including a very bright yellow light, about 15 centimetres in diameter, that suddenly appeared on the hillside no more than 150 metres from where he was on the road. The *Daily Mirror* reporter also saw mysterious lights along the same road that evening: a 'soft shimmering radiance' spread out across the road, illuminating every stick and stone within about 20 metres before fading away (*Daily Mail*, 13 February, 1905).

Reporters and other witnesses saw other remarkable lights near Egryn Chapel during the next few days. The *Daily Mirror*

man saw, from about 460 metres away, a very bright light near
the chapel. As he approached it, the light took the form of a
brilliant blue bar extending across the road. A quivering
radiance flashed from one end of the bar to the other and then
the light disappeared. A clergyman saw a mass of white light
rushing towards Egryn Chapel; taking the shape of 'a solid
triangle with rounded edges' it first hovered near one corner of
the chapel, then described an arc in the air and settled on the
opposite corner of the chapel before disappearing (*Daily Mirror*,
14 February 1905).

On 13 March 1905, a local Baptist minister, H.D. Jones, who
was following Mary Jones' car on foot after a meeting in a local
schoolhouse, saw a light appear in the road and dance around a
few yards in front of her car. When they reached the crossroads
at Llanbedr, the light took the left turn towards Egryn, as if
knowing which direction the car would have to take. Shortly
afterwards, the clergyman saw a small red ball of light, around
which two white lights danced.

Could this astonishing display of lights have been linked to a
nearby inactive fault? The lights in fact closely followed the trace
of the Mochras Fault.[24] This major structure runs southwards
from near Harlech through ancient Cambrian sedimentary rocks
to a point on the coast west of Barmouth. Moreover it is possible
that the lights were connected in some way with regional
seismic activity – there were several earthquakes in northwest
Wales during the fourteen-year period that culminated in the
1904–1905 outbreak of lights.

Many other parts of the world, too, Devereux found, seem to
have been haunted by mysterious light balls at various times.
For instance, in the early years of the century, one such ball was
seen emerging from a bay on Loch Torridon, Scotland, near
Shieldaig village. We may recall that it was precisely here that
Dr Fidler located many 'Earth energy lines', which, as we saw,
correlated well with local dykes and faults. Indeed, there is a
swarm of basic dykes close to the very point where the light ball
was seen.

There are many reports of similar light balls from other
localities in the British Isles. But it is from the USA that the most
detailed eye witness accounts have come. One well-known
American locality for observing such lights is about 11
kilometres east of Marfa, on Highway 90 in south-west Texas.
Since the late 1800s, people had seen dancing lights appear in
the distance to the south-west, in the direction of the Chinati
Mountains.

On the evening of 20 March 1973, two geologists working in
the area decided to try and get a closer look at some lights

cavorting in the distance. They drove towards the lights without headlights – it was a moonlit night – and then stopped. Soon they saw a light about 300 metres away cross the road about one metre above the ground. It then moved to the east and seemed to merge with another bright light. Then a third light approached the road, following the same path as the first light. The two geologists tried to approach it, but the light appeared to take evasive action, veering to the north so that when it crossed the road it was about 60 metres away from them. The light, about half the size of a basketball, moved to the north of the road, hovered there, and after about 30 seconds moved off to join the other lights. Finally, all the lights vanished together.

While possible links between the Marfa lights and local faults have not yet been established, there may be some connection with regional seismic activity – the light-haunted locality is close to one of the few earthquake epicentres in Texas.[25] But a link with both faulting and earth tremors does seem to exist in the case of another American locality haunted by mystery light balls – in this case a single ball of light – the Washington township, New Jersey.

For many years people reported seeing a luminous sphere about 45 centimetres in diameter moving along a stretch of old railway track. This so-called 'Hooker light' swayed from side to side as it moved and was believed to be the ghostly lantern of a dead train guard looking for his arm, which had been severed along this stretch of track. When the railway line was pulled up, the mystery light ball continued to appear.

Researchers investigating this weird light found two correlations of interest. Individual appearances of the 'Hooker' light ball, New Jersey, were apparently followed by earth tremors a few days later, while yearly variations in the light's performance seemed to correlate with activity within the nearby Ramapo fault system.[26]

A similar light accompanied by an almost identical legend is reputed to have haunted another stretch of railway track in the USA: near Maco Station, west of Wilmington, North Carolina, since the 1860s. It apparently starts with a flicker, grows brighter, and then gathers speed along the track, swaying from side to side and remaining about one metre above one of the rails. After travelling for about 100 metres, the light usually stops suddenly, hovers for a short time, then races back to its starting point, hovers again, and then disappears.

Again, while possible links with local faults have not been investigated, there is anecdotal evidence of a seismic connection.[27] From 1873 onwards, the light was reported to have a companion on its regular jaunts, but shortly after an earthquake in 1886, both lights disappeared for a period.

Such anecdotal evidence of links between light balls and seismicity has been supported by a series of statistical studies by Michael Persinger, of Laurentian University, Ontario, and John Derr, formerly of the US Geological Survey. Looking at 'UFO flaps' that had occurred in the Uinta Basin, Utah in 1967[28]; the Yakima area, Washington State in the 1970s;[29] and around Carman, Manitoba, during 1974–1977[30] the two researchers found that people tended to see fire balls and other strange lights weeks to months *before* numbers of small earthquakes increased regionally.

So there is already some evidence that enigmatic balls of concentrated energy may appear not only near active faults before major local earthquakes, but also near inactive faults at other times, their appearances possibly correlating in some way with regional seismic activity. All this suggests that the concept of a 'dowsable Earth energy line' is not quite as daft as it seems. Certain faults and related structures such as dykes and mineral veins not only give rise to subtle influences – magnetic changes, ionizing radiation and so on – that might loosely be called energies. From time to time, it now seems, these structures or the rocks nearby emit light balls, shimmering with undeniable energy.

What is the source of the Earth energy that powers these extraordinary balls of light? The seismic link suggests that the ultimate source of the energy lies in the stressed rocks of the Earth's crust. For scientists now know that immense forces are constantly straining at the rocks beneath our feet. Radioactive heating stirs the rocks of the Earth's interior into ceaseless motion just as the sun's heat causes winds to blow in the atmosphere, only the rocks move much more slowly. These sluggish but inexorable rock currents keep the Earth's continental crust under continual, usually compressive, stress.[31]

To explain the apparent time link between fire balls or other mystery lights and small earthquakes, Persinger and Derr have postulated that waves of stress and strain may sweep through sectors of continental crust, triggering off first light phenomena and then quakes. While this idea has not yet been proved, there certainly seems to be some time link between changes in local rock stress and the appearance of these mysterious balls of energy.

But why should they appear near old, inactive faults? It is plausible that one or more of the fault-linked influences that dowsers seem to detect with their supersenses play a rôle in transmuting the energy of stressed rocks into fire balls. Precisely which influences they are and how they interact with each other to generate light balls is a matter for speculation.

Electromagnetic fields seem a prime candidate – the attraction of light balls to metallic conductors such as steel rails suggests that the balls have an electromagnetic component. Japanese scientists have shown that when stressed in the laboratory, granite rock samples emitted bursts of electromagnetic radiation in the shortwave and microwave bands. The radiation was linked with the appearance of microcracks as the rocks underwent strain.[32] It therefore seems possible that, as they slowly deform, stressed rocks near faults may produce transient electromagnetic fields not only before earthquakes, but also at other times.

Fault-linked gases, such as radon, methane and other fuel gases, may also help to energize some of the mysterious balls of light. A group of researchers investigating the 'Hooker' light ball in New Jersey once recorded bursts of radioactivity, which they attributed to radon, when the ball disappeared.[33] Japanese researchers have created rudimentary fire balls in the laboratory by the ignition of mixtures of fuel gases with air (and combustible aerosol particles).[34]

In the case of mineralized faults, the crystal structure of minerals themselves may play a rôle in promoting fireball formation. Certain semi-conducting ore minerals found in polymetallic ores may help to transmute the energy locked up in stressed rocks into balls of fire.[35]

But of all the fault-linked influences that may help to transform the energy of stressed rocks into light balls perhaps the key could be the one that seems so important in dowsing – earth vibrations. Helmut Tributsch has proposed that such vibrations could catalyse the formation of fire balls by means of what is known technically as parametric energy conversion.[36] The idea is that if rocks vibrate at precisely the right frequency, an enormous amplification of existing electrical or electromagnetic fields may suddenly take place.

As we have just seen, electromagnetic outbursts might be expected from time to time as strain builds up near a geological fault. If, by chance, earth vibrations happened to hit just the right note during one of these outbursts, the initial field might be amplified and the energy somehow stabilized in the form of a fire ball.

So, if Tributsch is right, the zones of enhanced earth vibrations and other dowsable influences or energies over certain old, inactive geological faults may be deeply implicated in the formation of those most enigmatic of all Earth energy phenomena – the light balls. It looks as if the ancient notions of energy forces such as *pneuma* or *ch'i* flowing through the Earth were not so very far from the truth after all. Energy contained within the stressed, vibrating rocks of the Earth's crust causes not only earthquakes, but also many strange and subtle effects, including the dowsing effect, that orthodox science has hitherto overlooked. This energy seems to be channelled along geological faults and fractures, sometimes emerging in the form of playful balls of light that, like their hazel dowsing rods, led the miners of old to hidden veins of metal ore.

12 Dowsing and the Crop Circles Mystery

An anthropologist studying the growth of new religious cults would find much of interest taking place each summer in the cornfields of southern England. In addition to the traditional midsummer celebrations at Stonehenge, she would be fascinated to see people performing an entirely new ritual in the cornfields themselves. Holding L-shaped dowsing rods in both hands, hierophants would be seen performing strange rites as they perambulated inside circular, swirled areas in ripening wheat, barley, or other crops.

With mounting interest, our observer would discover that the new rituals were already accompanied by a body of doctrine. The dowsers would explain that they were detecting the Earth energies that had in some mysterious way flattened the circles of corn. Moreover, they would add, these were the very same energies that flowed along ley lines, focusing on ancient sites such as Stonehenge. No wonder, then, that the mysterious crop circles were now forming close to the henges, barrows and other monuments erected by the prehistoric peoples of Wessex. The dowsable Earth energies known to, and perhaps exploited by, the ancients were now causing ever-more complex crop circle formations to appear on the ground.

She would find that some crop circle dowsers were making even stranger claims. Seeing in some of the circles and associated marks resemblances to Neptune's trident, the war-shield of Mars or symbols of other deities such as Pluto and the Greek Earth goddess, Gaia, dowsers were concluding that certain intelligences – perhaps the old gods themselves – were warning us Earthlings of impending ecological catastrophe unless we changed our ways.[1]

If this is indeed the case, one can only comment that those old reprobates, Neptune (Poseidon), Mars (Ares) and Pluto (Hades) must have changed beyond recognition since the time of Homer. In classical times, these gods revelled in debauchery, murder and pillage. That this bloodthirsty gang of greedy rapists should suddenly transform themselves into solemn environmentalists beggars belief.

In fact, some crop circle dowsers may have recognized the old gods' true nature more clearly. According to the archaeologist Michael Green,[2] several dowsers have detected sexual features associated with crop formations. A formation associated with Gaia turns out to be bisexual and, according to Green, crop circles associated with other deities may also be bisexual or even hermaphrodite. This certainly makes more sense: Zeus, Apollo and other gods were renowned for their sexual conquests of both males and females. If the gods of classical antiquity really are using the sign language of crop circles to tell us something, it is far more likely to be about sex than ecology.

Looking at the weird dowsing rituals and the even weirder theories surrounding them, our anthropologist would almost certainly conclude that all the hallmarks of a new religious cult were present. Dismissing the circles themselves as hoaxes, she would argue that the dowsers were obviously moving their rods in response to nothing more energetic than their own subconscious imaginings.

While conceding that this conclusion is true in many cases, a more careful investigator of the crop circles phenomenon would have to admit that something very mysterious actually was going on. For a start, while many circles – particularly the highly complex groups that have appeared since 1990 – have indeed been made by hoaxers, others, such as those recorded before the phenomenon received massive publicity in the late 1980s, are without doubt genuine.[3, 4, 5, 6] As for dowsing, any serious student of the crop circles enigma would have to note that Dr Terence Meaden, the British physicist and meteorologist acknowledged as the leading authority on the subject not only regards dowsing as a potentially valuable tool in circles research, but has also used it himself.[7]

In the light of what we have found about some dowsers' ability to exploit their unconscious Sphinx-like supersenses, this does not seem an unreasonable attitude. If mysterious energies are swirling down into the crop fields of England and elsewhere, they might well be expected to leave traces in the soil that could be detected by one or more of the dowsers' supersenses.

In fact, dowsers first obtained responses over strange markings in cornfields as long ago as the summer of 1963. In the middle of July that year, Reg Alexander, a farmworker at Manor Farm, Charlton, Wiltshire, discovered a crater that had mysteriously appeared near the boundary between a potato field and a field of barley. The crater was a saucer-shaped depression in the soil, about 2.4 metres in diameter and 10 centimetres deep. At the centre of the crater was a small hole, while just outside it, radiating away from the hole, were four slot-like indentations in the soil, each about 1.2 metres long (see diagram opposite). All traces of vegetation had disappeared from the crater, while plant growth had been affected within a radius of about 6 metres from the central hole.[8]

On seeing the perplexing crater and markings that had appeared on his land, Roy Blanchard, the owner of Manor Farm, notified the police, who in turn called in Captain John Rogers, of the Army Bomb Disposal Unit, based at Horsham in Sussex. Captain Rogers and his men were completely baffled, but nevertheless started to investigate, using their metal-detecting equipment. According to one report, the instrument's needle behaved wildly, according to another the readings suggested that a large metal object might have embedded itself in the ground.

The mysterious crater in Mr Blanchard's field, and the possibility that something from outer space had landed there, were widely publicized in the press. My father, recently returned from his dowsing exploits in East Africa, and myself, then a student about to embark on a geology degree course at Oxford University, decided to visit the site and see if the crater was accompanied by a dowsing zone. We made several visits and did indeed experience dowsing responses within a roughly circular area extending about 10 metres from the central crater.[9]

But what had caused the crater and left an apparently dowsable trace in the soil? A mysterious Dr Robert Randall popped up on television to explain that a three-legged spaceship from Uranus had landed in the field for repairs. Patrick Moore, already well-known for his popular books and television broadcasts on astronomy, was quoted in several newspapers as suggesting that a more plausible object from outer space – a meteorite – had landed at Manor Farm and caused the crater.

On 25 July 1963, my father and I met Patrick Moore and Roy Blanchard at the crater site to discuss the latest evidence. The Bomb Squad had by then unearthed a small lump of stone in the soil, which they thought might have been responsible for their metal detector's signals. Patrick Moore could not confirm that the stone was a meteorite (in fact stony meteorites can look like ordinary stones) and it was sent to the British Museum (Natural History) for identification. Despite this uncertainty, Moore clung stoutly to his meteorite theory, explaining the dowsing results by suggesting that the object could have broken up on impact, scattering dust over the dowsing zone.

Unfortunately for the meteorite idea, the Museum soon identified the lump of stone as an ordinary piece of ironstone,

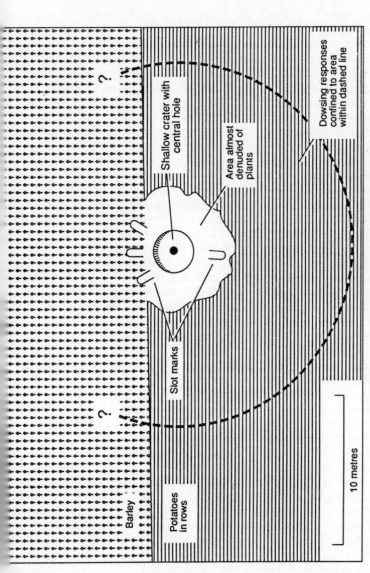

Fig.5 Mysterious marks found on a Wiltshire farm on 16 July 1963

common enough in the soils of this district.[10] Although it is just conceivable, as Patrick Moore suggested to us at the time, that the putative meteorite could have volatilized or remained buried in the soil, this could hardly explain the mysterious pattern of radial slots.

So if neither a spaceship from Uranus nor a meteorite from elsewhere in the solar system had landed on Roy Blanchard's farm, leaving a strange, apparently dowsable pattern in the soil, what had? One clue may lie in a remarkable experience reported by Frank Selwood, of Parkstone, Dorset (about 40 kilometres southeast of Charlton). At about 3 a.m. on Sunday 14 July, Mr Selwood looked out of his bedroom window and saw 'a large cigar-shaped object as big as four terrace houses' hovering about 100 metres above a large gasholder nearby. Frank Selwood saw what appeared to be a flashing wavy blue-green light in the middle of the object and could hear 'a quiet sort of whistle coming from it and flapping sounds'. It sounded to him rather like a broken-down dynamo. After hovering for about two-and-a-half minutes, the flashing light became continuous along the object's entire length, and, emitting a sound like a motor springing into life, the object 'made off to the west at fantastic speed'.[11]

Of course, we cannot be sure that Frank Selwood's frightening experience had anything to do with the Charlton crater and its dowsable crop marks. But thanks to the efforts of meteorologists and serious UFO researchers there are now on file hundreds of reported experiences like that of Frank Selwood, some even more bizarre and terrifying.

For example, at 11 p.m. on 28 March 1965, a dark and foggy night, Mr Eric Payne, then 19, was walking into the village of Bishopstrow, Wiltshire, when he heard 'a whistling noise that developed into a loud buzzing'. Although the noise sounded rather like the kind of humming that comes from telegraph wires in the wind, the humming was not coming from the wires. Then something seemed to be flattening the treetops on either side of the road and Eric Payne heard a 'tremendous racket' overhead. Looking up to see if it was a low-flying aircraft, he felt 'great pressure on my head and neck. Something stung my hands and cheeks. I lifted my fists and tried to fight it off'. He felt a prickling sensation, as though sharp needles were digging into his flesh. A knife-edged wind tore through his hair and burned at his eyes. The terrifying object was now making 'a jarring clatter, jumble and clanging that no plane could ever make'. Eric Payne's head was pushed from side to side and he said:

> I might as well have left my arms and legs at home for all the use they were. I simply could not stop this tremendous downward

pressure. I crawled round in the road for a bit and then sank to my knees on the grass verge, which was soaking wet. But that did not worry me. All I wanted was to get rid of the choking hold the thing had on me.

In the end the wind stopped and Eric Payne made his way home.[12]

Several unnerving experiences of a similar nature have been reported near the now notorious Colloway Clump bend in the A350 road just north of Warminster on the road to Westbury, Wiltshire. At 3.36 a.m. on 10 August 1965, a southbound truck driver was rounding the bend when he encountered a ball of crimson light. While breaking, the ball appeared to fasten on to his windscreen. Despite enormous vibrations, the glass did not break, but the driver nevertheless lost control and the truck ended up by some wire fencing on the other side of the road. The driver then saw a huge, bright circle, perhaps 9 to 12 metres across, detach itself from his truck and spin away with a whistling sound.[13]

About a month later, another disturbing incident at the same bend north of Warminster took place before dark between 7 and 7.30 p.m. on the evening of 7 September 1965. Major Hill was passing the bend in top gear when his engine cut out and his car came to a halt, shuddering 'under the down-beating pressure of aerial vibrations'. After a time, the convulsions of the car subsided enough for him to be able to jump out, only to experience violent air vibrations surrounding him and beating down on him, accompanied by a sinister whining and crackling. The noise sounded like 'high-powered refrigeration units or deep-freeze equipment, but far above that level, magnified many times'. After less than three minutes, everything was back to normal and Major Hill was able to drive away as if nothing had happened.[14]

While there is no direct evidence linking these particular frightening encounters with crop circles, it is surely no coincidence that many circles have since been found in the fields near Colloway Clump. An aerial photograph taken in July 1988 shows two circles very close to the bend, with a third only 200 metres away.[15]

An equally unnerving experience in the same area many years later was reported by a citizen-band radio enthusiast.[16] In order to pursue his hobby, the man regularly drove at night to high ground near Westbury, Wiltshire. Around 1 a.m. on 23 January 1988, a clear frosty night, his radio suddenly went dead. Thinking that a fuse must have blown, the man tried to start his car in order to return home. But he could not start it because the ignition failed. He soon heard a humming noise and then noticed a glow developing above the car. The light, white in the centre but orange at the edges, intensified, brightly illuminating an area at least ten metres in diameter. After about ten seconds the light seemed to diffuse away. Terrified, he tried to start the car again, the ignition now worked and he was able to drive home.

In other cases, though, people have encountered similar phenomena that *have* left circles behind. A classic occurrence of this kind took place on a large estate in Australia about 8 kilometres from Rosedale, Victoria on 30 September 1980.[17] At about 1 a.m. on a moonlit night, George Blackwell, the caretaker of the estate, was disturbed by the cattle, and then heard a screeching and whistling sound. Going outside to investigate, he was amazed to see a domed UFO with a 'white top' and 'orange and blue lights on its surface' slowly moving past a hay shed towards an uncovered concrete water tank about 500 metres away. The UFO appeared to climb on to the tank and then hovered there for about a minute before rising up again and then finally landing some way beyond the tank.

George Blackwell quickly changed, mounted his motorcycle and within five minutes was riding towards the object still hovering and whistling on the ground. About fifteen metres away from the object, the caretaker felt a curious sensation, 'like a plate of jelly' and could see circular windows or lights around the orange base, which was rotating in an anticlockwise direction. After a couple of minutes, the whistle increased to 'an awful scream' that hurt George Blackwell's ears. Something like a black tube appeared around the base of the object, inflated to a huge size, and then to the accompaniment of a bang the object emitted a blast of hot air that nearly flattened Blackwell.

The thing now rose slowly; with his motorcycle headlights the caretaker could see that the black tube had shrunk and that 'six spokes' now emerged from the centre of the base. The object rose in the air, depositing a rain of stones, weeds and cow dung in its wake and then disappeared silently to the east.

George Blackwell returned home quite stunned by the encounter, suffered headaches and nausea and was unable to sleep. He also found that his watch would not work when he wore it. In the morning he returned to the site and found a crop ring in the grass about 8 metres in diameter and 40 centimetres wide, flattened in an anticlockwise direction. Although the yellow flowering grass had been removed from the inner circle, radiating from the centre were six 'spokes', where the grass was almost undamaged. Later, it was found that all the water in the concrete tank had disappeared.

Another well-documented and revealing case concerns a West Yorkshire policeman, Alan Godfrey.[18] At 5.05 a.m. on 28 November 1980, PC Godfrey was driving through the outskirts of the small town of Todmorden, situated in the Pennine Hills. It had rained much of the night, but the weather was now clearing. The policeman was looking for some cows that had been disturbing the local residents when suddenly, on the road ahead, he saw something that was certainly no cow. It appeared like a glowing, spinning top and seemed to be accompanied by a wind that was moving the branches of nearby roadside trees. Alan Godfrey tried to use his radio to call base, but could not make it work. Then he experienced a memory lapse: his next recollection was of being further down the road and staring into an empty sky. Together with a colleague, PC Godfrey then inspected the site where the thing had hovered; they found a swirled circular pattern in the dry road surface. When PC Godfrey reported his sighting, he learned that other police officers had seen a bluish glow in the sky in the area at about the time he had seen the glowing object on the road.

A similar luminous, spinning, phenomenon that left circles behind was seen near Silbury Hill in Wiltshire in the middle of the night 28 to 29 June 1989.[19] Soon after midnight, the occupier of a cottage by the path leading to the prehistoric burial mound known as West Kennett Long Barrow saw a large spinning orange ball of light about 400 metres away to the west. The object descended into a field of wheat, its base appearing to flatten as it contacted the crop. The witness saw the object bounce and then disappear seven or eight seconds later. Next morning the witness saw a group of circles near the position where the light ball had hit the crop.

Terence Meaden arrived at the site on the morning of 30 June and found a remarkable group of circles in the field, including not only a large ringed circle but a beautiful quintuplet formation in which a large central circle was surrounded by four satellites.

Taken by themselves, these sometimes disturbing accounts might suggest that spacecraft from other worlds, perhaps even Uranus, are indeed visiting the Earth and leaving their circular landing marks behind. But before jumping to such a conclusion, we need to consider the most important evidence of all. For some people have observed circles forming during daylight, when they could see clearly what was happening.

For example, one fine evening in early August 1983, Melvyn Bell was riding a horse on the slopes of Great Cheverill Hill, in the north of Salisbury Plain.[20] He noticed dust spiralling up from a field of wheat about 50 metres away. As he watched, a circle, 10–12 metres in diameter formed in the wheat. It happened very quickly, within about two seconds, and for some moments afterwards dust and other debris spun up into the air and fell back again, chiefly around the edge of the circle.

About a year before this, in early July 1982, Ray Barnes saw a large circle form in a field at Westbury, Wiltshire.[21] About six in the evening, while it was still raining after a heavy thunderstorm, Mr Barnes saw what looked like a wave moving through the heads of the cereal crop. After crossing the field in a shallow arc, the wave or line suddenly appeared to pivot about one end and described a huge circle about 50 metres in diameter. While this was happening, Ray Barnes could hear a humming sound.

More recently, Sandy Reid, a naturalist interested in foxes, saw a circle form near Dundee, Tayside, Scotland.[22] Just after dawn one morning, probably 27 or 28 August 1989, Mr Reid was walking along an embankment between two sloping fields planted with spring barley. Suddenly he heard an unusual noise and a violent rustling in the corn nearby. With the reflex of an experienced naturalist, he instantly froze and adopted a crouching posture. Soon he realized that it was no animal but a localized movement of air that was affecting a circular area of corn. Then, quite quickly, the crop went flat within a circle about 15–18 metres in diameter. He entered the flattened circle and noticed that the straws had been laid down in a complex fashion, first one way and then the other. At the same time, he sensed an 'unusual condition in the atmosphere' – everything had gone quiet and even the birds had stopped singing.

These eyewitness accounts suggest that crop markings such as the Charlton crater and many of the more recent crop circles are not made by spaceships from Uranus, bisexual gods, or even mysterious Earth energies emerging above ley lines, but by a hitherto unrecognized atmospheric phenomenon.

At first this may be very difficult for us to accept. For how could such a disorderly substance such as moving air create precise, sharp-edged circles? How could air emit those weird humming noises, or give rise to rotating lights? And how could air in motion have interfered with automobile ignition systems, radio equipment and possibly left behind dowsable traces in the ground? One man – Dr Terence Meaden – has the answers.[23]

Meaden first draws our attention to the remarkable features of several recognized, though not yet properly understood atmospheric phenomenon. One has been traditionally called ball lightning, though even this may be a misnomer in that these balls of light have often been seen in fair weather conditions as well as during thunderstorms.[24] Many witnesses have described seeing these light balls, whose odd behaviour has sometimes rivalled that of the Earth-born lights described in the last chapter.

For instance, William Becker, a professor of industrial design at the University of Illinois, related the following account.[25] During the summer of 1956, Becker, then a high school student, was on a canoeing trip with school friends in an area of ancient copper ore deposits north of the town of Grand Marais, Minnesota. The weather turned foul, with pouring rain, so the boys sought refuge in a deserted cabin. Becker and a friend shared the back room of the cabin. As the cabin was stuffy after the daytime heat, Becker opened the window a crack and saw what looked like a flashlight moving around in the darkness outside. To the boys' amazement, the light then began to squeeze through the open crack above the window sill into the room. They saw a ball of light, just larger than a basketball, float into the room. The ball appeared to have an orange core surrounded by a brighter, yellow-white outer perimeter and as it silently passed close by Becker, he could see what looked like 'worms' or short strings of light writhing at its centre. The ball slowly descended towards an old Indian-style black-and-white rug on the floor. Then, unbelievably, the ball moved slowly over the rug, tracing the dark patterns on the rug as it did so. It thereupon proceeded towards the far corner of the room, shrank in size and appeared to escape through the boards. Finally, as Becker and his friend turned towards each other to scream their amazement at what had happened, they heard a sharp report, 'like a loud firecracker'. The next morning the boys found a broken drainpipe outside the cabin wall, where the explosion had taken place. Discussing this extraordinary event afterwards, Becker and his friend concluded that lightning had in some way interacted with the copper deposits to produce the ball.

Another barely credible description of a light ball was one of many collected by Dr Terence Meaden's research group.[26] Just after midnight one night, probably in 1969, a married couple, Elsie and Doug Hawdon were in bed in their bungalow near Manchester, England. Having been woken up by a thunderstorm, they were amazed to see a silent, fast-spinning, orange-yellow fire ball slowly enter the bedroom through the open doorway leading to the hall. The sharp-edged, bright ball of light, about one metre in diameter and emitting red sparks, stopped and then retreated back along the hall before disappearing. Alarmed that the ball might have also invaded their son's bedroom, the couple dashed along the hallway to find a slight 'electrical' smell but no damage and their son sleeping like a log in his bed.

The balls are not always so harmless. Dr George Egely, of the

Central Institute of Physics, Budapest, a ball lightning expert, reported the following incident.[27] On 25 May 1989, a 27-year-old engineer, accompanied by his wife was driving along a road near the village of Kerecseud, 109 kilometres from Budapest. Although the weather was dry at the time, they had recently driven through a thunderstorm. Feeling the need to urinate, the man stopped his car and walked about ten metres to the edge of a field. Suddenly his wife, who had remained in the car, saw a blue light surround her husband, who then opened his arms wide and fell to the ground. At the same time she saw that one of his shoes had come off. The woman at once ran to try and save her husband, but to no avail. She stopped a passing bus, which turned out to be full of doctors returning from a meeting. The doctors pronounced the man dead and at the autopsy a hole was found in the man's heel where the shoe had been, the lungs were torn and damaged and the stomach was found to be carbonized. Dr Egely concluded that the light ball had passed into the body of the unfortunate man, who thereupon experienced partial internal combustion.

These extraordinary balls of light, capable even of homicide, were composed of nothing but air – albeit probably in the form of ionized air or plasma, and associated with strong electromagnetic fields. So it is by no means impossible that the rotating, humming, luminous objects that have astonished witnesses from England to Australia were likewise composed of air.

Another relevant atmospheric phenomenon is the tornado. Those witnesses fortunate enough to have survived close encounters with these violent vortices of air have sometimes reported remarkable phenomena. Some have seen tornado funnels ablaze with light, like self-illuminated tubes. One tornado funnel, seen in Oklahoma, USA, in May 1955 was marked by a waist-like rotating band of blue light, while the ground beneath it emitted a luminous discharge.[28] This tornado also gave off intense radio-frequency electromagnetic emissions that were accompanied by optical flashes and monitored by staff at the Stillwell Tornado Laboratory.

There are also accounts of tornadoes ejecting ball lightning 'like hens laying eggs' while in 1872 four people who witnessed the Newbottle tornado in Northamptonshire heard a whizzing, roaring sound like a passing train and then saw the tornado itself in the form of a huge, revolving ball of fire travelling about two metres above the ground.

So, ball lightning and tornadoes show that recognized phenomena in Earth's atmosphere can produce whirring sounds, luminous effects, intense electromagnetic radiation, electrical discharges, can eject balls of fire or even appear as rotating balls of light. We have already encountered mysterious Earth-born light balls, apparently energized by stressed, vibrating rocks, and it now seems that atmospheric vortices can generate similar phenomena. The atmospheric vortices, however, derive their energy not from Earth's radioactively heated interior, but from its sun-heated atmosphere. In both cases the energy content of a huge volume of Earth material – rocks or air – is somehow focused into a tiny volume – with remarkable consequences.

But how is this energy stabilized in the form of light balls? Until recently, the physics of ball lightning remained a complete mystery. However, in 1991 Y.H. Ohtsuki and H. Ofuruton succeeded in creating artificial coloured fire balls in air by the interference of short radio waves (microwaves).[29] The balls consisted of glowing plasma – air that had been ionized by the focused microwave energy. While the balls persisted for a few seconds only, they did show some of the remarkable characteristics of ball lightning. One passed through a ceramic board in a ghostly way and others moved against the flow of air.

To maintain their small plasma fire balls, the Japanese researchers had to constantly supply energy, at the rate up to 5 kilowatts of power, in the form of microwaves. But where could such focused energy come from under natural conditions?

Ohtsuki and Ofuruton gave several tantalizing hints. They suggested that different types of energy might interact in the atmosphere to generate fire balls. Their own experiments indicated that one of these energy sources could be electromagnetic waves and they propose that complex topography might cause such waves to interfere and focus the energy.

Could this ability of electromagnetic energy to transform common-or-garden air into exotic plasma or at least partially ionized air be the explanation not only for the remarkable behaviour of Earth-born light balls, ball lightning and known atmospheric vortices such as tornadoes, but the rotating, humming, luminous phenomena that have frightened people, stopped their cars and radios, and left behind circles or craters in crops and apparently dowsable traces in the soil? Terence Meaden certainly thinks so. In one of the most exciting contributions to science of recent times[30] he has proposed the existence of a hitherto unrecognized atmospheric phenomenon – the electrically charged circles-effect vortex.

Meaden argues that these vortices are typically generated in the lee of certain hills when a new air mass – for example, a sea-breeze front – encroaches into a volume of stable, stratified air. Vast amounts of energy may then be focused into systems of spinning vortex tubes, which, under certain conditions, may descend to the ground. The vortex's spin energy interacts with factors such as the existing electrostatic field, the presence of charged aerosol particles and water vapour to generate intense systems of rotating electrical charges. Some of the charge is likely to be carried by ionized molecules of air and if more than a certain proportion of air molecules is ionized, the air will behave as a plasma.

Profoundly sensitive to surrounding electric and electromagnetic fields, the Meaden vortex would in these circumstances show a sharp boundary with the surrounding electrically neutral air, just what is needed to create the precisely sculpted crop circles. It might move against the wind, and rush towards or hover over conducting objects such as cars or bodies of water. It would emit whirring noises in the same way as electrically charged whirlwinds such as dust devils do, and appear luminous in the dark, as excited air molecules emit photons when returning to their ground states. People like Eric Payne unfortunate enough to have been hit by a Meaden vortex and breathed its ionized air might well experience the 'serotonin stimulation syndrome' and suffer from nausea and headaches.

The ground traces left by a descending Meaden vortex system would vary with many factors, such as the velocity of descent. A gently descending vortex might just brush the top of the crops, leaving a shallow whirled impression behind while more rapidly descending vortices could press the crops to the ground very hard indeed. This may have happened at Chilcomb, near Winchester in 1987, where a large circle in wheat was found, completely flattened in a star-burst pattern. In extreme cases, the vortex might crash into the ground with enormous force, hollowing out a crater in the soil. Terence Meaden has suggested that this is precisely what may have happened at Manor Farm, Charlton, in early July, 1963.[31]

So after all these years, it seems that it was not a spaceship from Uranus, nor even, as Patrick Moore thought, a 'shrimp sized meteorite' that landed among Farmer Blanchard's potatoes, but a very rapidly descending Meaden vortex. But if this was the case, how can we explain the soil anomaly at the crater site that was apparently detected both by the Army Bomb Disposal Squad's equipment and by dowsing? Could it have been an early example of the same effect that has caused cars and radios to stop?

There is every reason to believe so. Not only would a vortex be accompanied by electrostatic fields and ionized air. Rotating electrical charges in the vortex would generate strong electromagnetic fields just as some tornadoes do. Singly or acting together, these factors might well be capable of interfering with automotive ignition systems and leaving traces in the soil detectable by instruments or dowsers.

One possibility might be that the magnetic fields of such vortices are strong enough to permanently alter the magnetic properties of minerals in the soil. Alternatively, the electrostatic charge left behind on the surface by a ground-impacting vortex might remain long enough to be sensed by a dowser. The presence of ionized air, too, might be expected to affect a dowser who visited a site very recently hit by a descending Meaden vortex.

To decide between these and other possibilities, controlled experiments are clearly needed. It may well be true that the majority of present-day crop circle dowsers are simply responding to the visual cues provided by the circles themselves. This would explain why dowsers have so far been unable to distinguish hoaxes from genuine circles. But if the ideas outlined in this chapter are broadly correct, the findings in Part I of this book suggest that a few experienced dowsers may indeed be able to detect tell-tale traces left by the exotic Meaden vortices.

If this is confirmed experimentally, the notion that crop circles are somehow connected with 'Earth energies' would be seen to contain a grain of truth after all. For the supersenses we unconsciously use in dowsing would then be shown to give us an awareness of a remarkable class of energies flowing through our planet that scientists have until now ignored. Descending in the form of atmospheric vortices, these influences buffet the boundary zone between Earth and air where we live and sometimes burst disturbingly into our lives.

13   Geopsychology

In tracing the controversial story of dowsing, from sixteenth-century mineral finders to crop circle dowsers of the 1990s, we have encountered several unexpected twists. Some of the dowsers' cherished beliefs – that mineral veins or water act directly on the rod, or that the dowsing reaction is a physiological response – have turned out to be false. Unaware of the rôle of suggestion in dowsing, many dowsers have fallen victim to self-deception, making claims they have been unable to substantiate.

Equally, we have seen that the dismissive attitude of sceptical scientists to all dowsing is unjustified. Over the centuries, a select band of outstanding dowsers like Hans Schröter have been remarkably successful in locating hidden geological faults and fractures that may be linked with minerals, radon, water and oil.

The most likely explanation for dowsing success, too, was unexpected. The notion that dowsers succeed by unconsciously responding to appropriate sensory cues was first suggested not by dowsers or their supporters but by their opponents – the sceptics. The novel feature that transformed a sceptics' argument into a sound theoretical basis for dowsing was the evidence that these cues include exotic influences sensed by animals such as changes in magnetism and Earth vibrations. Good dowsers, it seems, learn to exploit appropriate Sphinx-like supersenses, thereby outperforming professional Earth scientists who rely on conventional sensory information.

This discovery has exciting implications for all of us, whether we dowse or not. As the experiments of Robin Baker and Gai Murphy at the University of Manchester are showing, we seem to make use of our sense of magnetism in activities such as direction-finding, navigation and exploration. It therefore now seems likely that other exotic supersenses play important rôles in our lives. Moreover, it is probable that we unconsciously respond to a vast range of conventional sense data that is never presented to our conscious minds. A hidden but ever-changing world of invisible colours, inaudible sounds and, above all, unnoticed smells may underlie many apparently inexplicable shifts in our moods, feelings and emotions.

Of particular interest are the similarities between the mental attitudes needed for successful dowsing, 'seeing with our hands' and direction finding. In each case, if we calculate or consciously try to solve the problem, we fail. We do best by relaxing and simply guessing, thus making use of valuable supersensory information normally denied to the conscious, cerebrating parts of our brains. Further understanding of these hidden mental powers could pay handsome dividends not only in improving our dowsing abilities but also in developing other latent potentials.

Another finding has been that traditional dowsers' claims, long ridiculed by orthodox scientists, may actually contain a surprising amount of truth. Thus the dowsers of old believed that all underground water flowed in 'water veins'. Much to the annoyance of modern hydrogeologists, most present-day dowsers still do – ignoring the scientists' new understanding of how, under the influence of gravity, huge masses of ground water trickle slowly through the pore spaces of certain rocks. Yet, when we saw how seventeenth-century miners, accustomed to dowse for mineral veins, first applied their art to water-finding, the concept of 'water veins' seems quite logical. In fact the dowsers' old-fashioned notion of water veins or underground streams still does make sense in certain geological situations. The dowsers' term is merely an archaic way of describing what today's scientists would call 'water-bearing fracture zones', 'solution-fissures in limestone' and so on.

More surprisingly, the traditional belief of some dowsers that they could detect 'zones of harmful Earth rays' or 'black streams' turns out to have a parallel in a recent and somewhat alarming set of scientific findings that have not yet been digested by the media or public. If we are concerned about the effects of radioactivity on our health, we should forget about nuclear power stations and concentrate instead on preventing the radioactive, carcinogenic gas radon seeping into our homes from below. For recent research, by the National Radiological Protection Board in the United Kingdom and equivalent organizations in other countries has shown that, in certain regions, radon presents a grave threat to people's health. Quite unexpectedly, as we have seen, the limited data available now suggests that people's chances of succumbing to lung cancer, and perhaps other conditions, may be related more to the proximity of water-bearing faults and fracture zones than to the nature of the underlying rock. The fracture zones can be deadly because they conduct rising, radon-rich groundwater or radon gas to the surface. The analogy with the dowsers' 'black streams' or 'zones of harmful earth rays' is almost perfect.

Perhaps most unexpected of all, though, as we saw in chapter eleven, the New Age concept of dowsable Earth energies now seems to contain a modicum of scientific sense. To be sure, the new findings lend no support to many of those dowsers who claim to detect energy lines or centres. From what we now know about the rôle of suggestion in dowsing, it seems likely that most of these energy locations exist only in the imaginations of their finders.

But it is the exceptions that disprove the rule, and as we have found, *some* energy lines – for instance those that the late Dr J. Havelock Fidler, found in the Applecross peninsula of Scotland – most definitely *do* exist. Fidler's work suggests that instead of rejecting it out of hand, scientists may find the concept of 'dowsable Earth energy lines' a profitable one to examine.

To start with, the notion of a 'dowsable line' is not as trivial as it appears at first sight. The idea implies not only that different dowsers will respond in the same places but that such locations are not single spots or even general areas, but actual lines – or at least narrow linear zones. So the dowsers' concept is informative and, above all, testable. Moreover, in the light of the scientific investigations reported in this book, the idea fares surprisingly well. Though not rigorous by Western standards, the work of the Soviet and Romanian geologists, reported in chapter one, supports the notion that different dowsers do indeed respond in the same places and that, as Fidler found, these often take the form of narrow linear zones coinciding with geological faults, fracture zones or dykes. More importantly, the most thorough scientific investigation of dowsing ever carried out, funded by the Federal Government of Germany, showed that blindfolded dowsers independently showed responses immediately above a hidden geological fault.

If the New Agers' 'dowsable lines' correlate with certain geological faults and related features, we may perhaps equate their 'dowsable energies' with the subtle influences – such as magnetic and electromagnetic changes, increases in amplitude of Earth vibrations, increased emission of radon and other gases, gamma rays, air ionization, aerosols – above the faults. Although not strictly speaking energies in the scientific sense, it is not easy to think of a much better collective term for them. What they do have in common is that they are active influences that actually exist in the vicinity of certain faults and really do impart energy to the dowser's sense organs.

In chapter eleven, we found more tangible energies linked with particular faults. The miners of old firmly believed that hidden veins of metal ore might betray their presence by emitting 'fiery coruscations' or balls of fire. As we saw, there are many eyewitness accounts of light balls emerging from the ground and then disporting themselves in characteristic ways. These so-called Earth lights jump from one place to another, perform routine nightly displays and on occasion even try to evade the attentions of observers. We might be inclined to dismiss these reports as the inventions of publicity-seeking inebriates were it not for two things. There are impeccable reports of similar light balls appearing before earthquakes.[1] There are also numerous accounts of similar light balls performing in a similar fashion, but classified by scientists as 'ball lightning'.

Those light balls seen before earthquakes are clearly associated with active faults and we found evidence linking other Earth-born light balls with old, inactive geological faults. As the emission of light is an undeniable sign of the presence of energy, we were forced to conclude that certain geological faults and mineral veins (in other words mineralized faults) and the rocks nearby not only emit an array of active dowsable influences that might loosely be termed energies, but also, from time to time, disgorge packets of indisputable energy – Earth energy if you like – in the shape of mysterious balls of fire.

But the real surprise was that one of these dowsable influences – enhanced levels of earth vibrations – may be the key factor that from time to time triggers the release of large dollops of 'Earth energy' in the form of light balls. More speculatively, it is even possible that other dowsable influences – magnetic and electromagnetic field changes, radon, aerosols and so on – may be precisely the set of cofactors needed for energy release to take place.

If one kind of dowsable influence, Earth vibrations, may be linked to one kind of energy display, the Earth-born light ball, it now seems that another such influence, changed magnetic field strength, may be connected with the traces of another kind of energy release – the crop circle-forming Meaden vortex. Although these remarkable vortices derive their energy from processes in Earth's atmosphere rather than in its interior, the actual mechanisms involved are surprisingly similar. Just as slowly moving masses of hot rock deep within the Earth stress and energize the rocks beneath our feet, so fast-moving air masses in the atmosphere pump energy into the Meaden vortex. As we saw in chapter twelve, this energy may be focused so intensely as to convert ordinary air into exotic, ionized plasma. According to Terence Meaden, some vortices may evolve into luminous, rotating balls of light, accompanied by strong electromagnetic fields. It is this electromagnetic factor, apparently, that may enable a Meaden vortex to leave dowsable and instrumentally detectable traces behind in the ground.

Linked, as it is, both with playful Earth-born lights and these extraordinary luminous vortices, dowsing seems to be leading us forward to confront a whole new class of electromagnetically active and often fault-related Earth energy phenomena. The possibility therefore arises that such hitherto unrecognized releases of energy might be responsible for other little-understood effects. Perhaps such energy outbursts might help to explain some longstanding mysteries, for instance reports of hauntings and the alleged activities of those mischievous, destructive spirits known in German tradition as 'noisy ghosts' or poltergeists.

It has to be admitted that such notions are even more speculative than the other ideas floated in this book, and few scientists would even be willing to consider them. However, one scientist has ventured into this scientific quagmire. Professor Michael Persinger of Laurentian University, Sudbury, Ontario, the Canadian scientist whose studies of possible links between light balls and earthquakes were mentioned in chapter eleven, claims to have actually monitored electromagnetic events apparently associated with poltergeist hauntings.

Together with Robert Cameron, a geophysicist at Laurentian University, Persinger investigated one alleged poltergeist haunting in detail.[2] In 1975 two young women living in the mining city of Sudbury, Ontario, reported unusual disturbances in the apartment they were sharing. These usually happened after midnight, in the early hours of the morning. One morning, at about 4.20 a.m. a dish hanging on the kitchen wall suddenly fell and broke with a loud crash. This was followed soon afterwards by a noise like 'someone slamming a door'. Night after night both women heard further noises such as slammings and swishing sounds, while on several occasions one of the women (referred to as Miss N.) woke in the early hours to see human-like figures at the foot of her bed. One night, at about 3 a.m., Miss N. saw the figures again and feared that they might touch her. At about the same time, her boyfriend, who was sleeping with her, saw a small white circular light across the bedroom wall at the foot of the bed.

The women were so upset by these phenomena that they decided to move out of the apartment, Miss N. immediately and the other woman (referred to as Miss B.) at the end of the month. In the meantime the women allowed Persinger and Cameron to set up monitoring equipment in their apartment. The scientists connected two geophones (vibration sensors used in seismic exploration) to a chart recorder, the first near the bedroom wall where the light had been seen and the second in the hall. But whereas they linked the bedroom geophone directly to the recorder so that it would serve as a conventional vibration monitor, the investigators connected the hall geophone to the recorder by means of a wire coil, placed near the bedroom wall. In this way, the output from the hall geophone would monitor not only vibrations in the hall, but any large magnetic changes – which would induce current in the coil – in the bedroom.

Would the 'noisy ghost' reveal its secrets to the scientists' measuring devices? For ten nights Miss B., now occupying the room vacated by Miss N., slept undisturbed and no unusual events were recorded by the equipment. Then, early in the morning of 27 November, some strange things happened. Having gone to bed at about 12.30, only about a minute later Miss B. suddenly experienced intense fear. She got out of bed, phoned her boyfriend from a neighbour's flat and spent the rest of the night at his apartment.

When the researchers looked at the output from the chart recorder in the morning, they found that just when Miss B. had felt intense fear, the magnetic monitor had recorded a 10-second signal so strong that ink had been sprayed from the recorder and both recording pens had been bent. Because the signal from the magnetic monitor was so much stronger than that from the vibration monitor, Persinger and Cameron concluded that a brief, but intense electromagnetic event had taken place in the bedroom, precisely at the time when Miss B. had experienced sudden fear.

The scientists measured anomalous signals in the now unoccupied bedroom on one more occasion. On 30 November, at about 2 a.m., the magnetic monitor recorded two brief signals, each lasting between 5 and 10 seconds.

If the anomalous signals corresponded to real electromagnetic excursions, it is possible that sudden changes in electric fields could have led to some of the noisy activities of the poltergeist, for example displacing the dish hanging on the kitchen wall so that it crashed to the floor and causing doors to slam. But, if so, how did the electromagnetic events originate in the first place?

There are several clues to help us. The faint light ball seen in the haunted bedroom may imply a connection with other light ball incidents. Indeed, according to Persinger the Sudbury events coincided with a local 'UFO flap' which reached such a pitch that on 11 November 1975 a squadron of US National Guard F106 interceptors was scrambled from a nearby base.

The link with light ball sightings, which, as we have seen,

often seem to be fault-related, suggests that the presence of local faulting and mineralization may have been relevant. In fact the mining town of Sudbury is located on a major bowl-shaped body of iron and nickel-rich igneous rocks thought to have resulted from the impact of a giant meteorite here about two billion years ago. The haunted apartment was close to the southern contact between the igneous rocks and ancient metasediments – just over 200 metres north of the intersection of two small faults where copper and iron sulphide mineralization had occurred, and about 500 metres north of the major Creighton Fault.

Given that the local geological environment favoured the occurrence of electromagnetic events and light ball sightings, what actually triggered the releases of energy at particular times? One possible clue was provided by seismograph records at Laurentian University, about two kilometres from the haunted apartment. On 10 and 11 November 1975, the time of peak UFO and poltergeist activity, the seismograph recorded unusually large microseisms, at a frequency of around 0.8 Hertz. These were believed to have been caused by the passage of a weather system of exceptionally low pressure across the Sudbury area at the time.

Basing his speculations on the Sudbury case and other incidents, Persinger has put together a broad theory to explain the timing of sudden releases of energy in the form of light balls and other electromagnetic events. On his hypothesis, stress slowly builds up near certain faults. Then factors such as microseisms due to changes in air pressure, lunar tidal forces, or magnetic storms – interact with the system in such a way as to trigger release of the accumulated energy in sudden outbursts.

If these ideas are on the right lines, some kinds of poltergeist hauntings take their place with the dowsing effect and Earth-born light balls in a newly discovered class of fault-linked energy phenomena.

Now dowsing is a psychological effect, in which the dowser's sense organs and brain respond to subtle influences, including, it seems, small magnetic changes. The precise coincidence of the 10-second electromagnetic signal measured by Persinger and Cameron at Sudbury with Miss B's sudden fear raises the possibility that the brief but intense electromagnetic events linked with light ball or poltergeist phenomena can also affect the human brain.

In fact, there *is* evidence that some people who have had close brushes with luminous phenomena also experienced psycho-logical effects. Alan Godfrey, the Yorkshire policeman whose encounter with what was probably a Meaden vortex was related in chapter twelve, is one such person. After the amazed policeman tried to radio base (but without success, possibly due to electromagnetic interference) he experienced a memory lapse that was afterwards found to have lasted about ten minutes.[3] And his experience was not unique – several other people who have survived close encounters with lights have also reported memory gaps.

Some witnesses of strange lights have reported stranger things. In January 1970, two young men were skiing in a forest near Imjärvi, southern Finland.[4] They were terrified to see a circular luminous object in the sky, surrounded by a mist and emitting a buzzing noise. The object descended towards them, settling only a few metres from them, in a forest clearing. What they reported next defied belief. A small, pale-faced creature, with thin limbs and a hook for a nose, appeared and pointed a beam of light at the men. The light beam struck one of the men, then a mist swirled around and the luminosity disappeared. After the encounter, both men suffered physiological effects, including headaches and aching joints. One of them was initially paralysed on his right side and thereafter suffered from memory disturbances and other psychological effects.

Many other people who have reported close encounters with luminous phenomena have made equally astonishing claims. Moreover, starting in the 1960s, some UFO researchers found that under regression hypnosis, such witnesses could often 'remember' what had happened to them. Following PC Godfrey's encounter, for instance, a group of UFO investigators persuaded him to undergo such hypnosis. After several sessions, Alan Godfrey came up with an extraordinary story. During his blackout, Godfrey now recalled, he floated into a strange room and met a tall, bearded man who telepathically introduced himself as Yosef, some little robots and a big black dog.[5] The policeman suffered head and body pains which he interpreted as the results of a medical examination. This account is similar to those reported by many other witnesses of strange lights, who, under hypnosis, claim to have been abducted by aliens, taken on board their spaceships and medically examined.

What are we to make of all this? The stories told by eyewitnesses are far too silly to be taken as literal truth, yet in many cases, including Alan Godfrey's, there is independent evidence that the witness really did encounter a luminous phenomenon. Michael Persinger has suggested that in such cases, powerful electromagnetic fields associated with the light may have affected the electrical activity within the witnesses' brains, causing them to experience hallucinations.[6]

The most susceptible parts of the brain would be the temporal lobes – large areas of cortex on either side of the brain – and two connected underlying structures, the hippocampus and amygdala. The temporal lobes appear to be involved in many important brain functions, including perceptual processing, and even consciousness, while the hippocampus is concerned with memory and the amygdala with emotions. Electrical stimulation of these brain structures can evoke a range of memories, sensations, hallucinations and meaningful or dream-like experiences. Moreover, electrical seizures within the temporal lobes can cause certain kinds of epileptic fits. During such attacks, the sufferer may see visions, hear voices or experience dream-like states.

Bearing all this in mind, Persinger speculated that if light balls come close enough to people, their electromagnetic fields may provoke the same kinds of hallucinations and other mental experiences as electrical stimulation or epileptic seizures. The content of the experience, would, as in dreams, express themes and imagery already present in the percipient's brain.

The notion that Earth's naturally occurring electromagnetic fields might not merely be detectable by our senses, as in dowsing, but might also affect the actual functioning of our brains is not a new one. As we saw in chapter ten, Professor G. Ruhenstroth-Bauer, of the Max Planck Institute for Biochemistry, Munich, one of the scientists involved in the recent German dowsing investigation, has discovered statistical correlations between the onset of epileptic seizures and the emission of radio-frequency electromagnetic waves by moving air masses in the atmosphere.[7]

Another of the German dowsing investigators, Professor Herbert König, noting the similarity in frequencies between Earth's low-frequency Schumann electromagnetic broadcasts and the alpha rhythms of our own brains, suggested that variations in the Schumann transmissions might influence human brain operation. Recent work by Persinger and his colleagues suggests that König may have been right – Schumann waves probably do interact with our brains, albeit weakly. In one series of experiments, the Canadian scientists found that weak 5Hz electromagnetic fields, applied along the plane of the temporal lobe, influenced subjects' recall memory and ability to relax.[8]

In more recent experiments[9] volunteers wore helmets that exposed their temporal lobes to weak (30–100 nanoteslas) Schumann frequency (4-16Hz) magnetic fields. The scientists found that these fields seemed to increase the tendency of subjects to report the kind of experiences associated with epileptic seizures – dream-like states, visions and so on. In one set of experiments particularly relevant to encounters with light balls, the fields seemed to increase subjects' readiness to dream up UFO abduction scenarios of the kind reported by Allen Godfrey.

So it seems that certain weak, low-frequency magnetic fields can actually influence the thoughts and ideas passing through our minds. It does not need much imagination to envisage the applications, some of them horrific, that might stem from this discovery. But, as far as light balls are concerned, the implications are literally mind-boggling.

The artificial magnetic fields so far applied experimentally have been not only very weak, but also not of the optimum kind to interact with our brains. Could the far stronger, pulsing fields associated with some Meaden vortices and other light balls perhaps mimic the neuronal firing patterns of temporal lobe structures, thereby evoking dream-like experiences, hallucinations and memory lapses in the way that Michael Persinger suggested? The presence of electrostatic fields, ionized air, aerosols and so on might also play a part in inducing such effects. Perhaps Alan Godfrey and other people who have claimed to have been abducted by occupants of UFOs were telling the truth, as they remembered it, after all.

This exciting idea suggests an even more startling possibility. If the complex, pulsating magnetic fields associated with light balls can influence the firing patterns of neurons in our brains, could the process be reversed? In other words, could our thoughts actually influence the behaviour of some light balls, thereby accounting for the reports of balls apparently responding to witness's actions or intentions? Paul Devereux first speculated along such lines as long ago as 1982[10] when the notion appeared so crazy as to brand him an extreme member of the lunatic fringe. As we will see shortly, however, new ideas are appearing on the horizon that make this idea seem less shocking now.

Before looking at this new thinking though, let us now take stock of what we have found. Our investigation of dowsing has led us to recognize a class of typically fault-linked Earth energy phenomena that seem capable of interaction with the human brain. At the low-energy end of this geopsychological spectrum, small changes in magnetism, Earth vibrations or other influences are detected by the sense organs and the brain instructs relevant muscles to move, initiating the dowsing response. At the high-energy end, occasional large electromagnetic disturbances appear to influence firing patterns of neurons in the temporal lobe, inducing hallucinations or other mental experiences.

In chapter eleven we noted the analogy between the subtle, dowsable influences or occasional energy releases associated with some geological faults and ancient holistic notions of energizing fluids like *ch'i* and *pneuma*. Now, with the extension of these newly discovered energy effects to include the electromagnetically active Meaden vortices, and the apparent ability of all these phenomena to interact with human brains, the analogy seems even closer.

This parallelism between ancient holistic notions and modern scientific findings forces us to consider again the question of how far reductionist scientific analysis can illuminate these complex energy conversion processes and their even more complicated geopsychological effects. Of course, investigators working on conventional lines will continue to make progress. For example, evidence is building up that tiny rock cracks, generally filled with water as Helmut Tributsch suggested, play an important rôle in upper crustal energy flows.[11] As we have seen, by subjecting granite samples to increasing stress, Japanese scientists found that just as tiny new cracks formed, the rocks emitted outbursts of electromagnetic energy at radio frequencies.[12] This process is not yet properly understood, but the fact that it can now be demonstrated in the laboratory suggests that scientists will soon have a better understanding of how stressed, vibrating rocks from time to time release bursts of energy that may take the form of electromagnetically active balls of light.

Approaching the light ball problem from the complementary viewpoint of atmospheric physics, further work by Professor Yoshihiko Ohtsuki, Dr Terence Meaden and others should help plasma vortex theory explain eyewitness reports of luminous phenomena and their electromagnetic effects. At the same time, we may hope that other scientists will join Michael Persinger in studying how the magnetic fields associated with light balls and vortices may interact with our brains.

Related to all these studies will be further investigations of the psychological and pathological effects of geological faults. For, both the low-energy dowsable influences and the sudden, high-energy outbursts that seem to be linked with faults are likely to have insidious long-term effects on human beings. While emission of the carcinogenic gas radon is almost certainly the most dangerous of these effects, there may be other malign influences. For instance, Persinger has pointed out that the powerful magnetic fields associated with fault-linked light balls or poltergeist phenomena may not only have carcinogenic effects but, if repeated, also play a part in inducing psychiatric disorders such as depression. Such conditions might result from the effects of magnetic fields on temporal lobe activity and melatonin synthesis in the brain.[13]

To help achieve a better understanding of all these effects on human beings, further studies of how dowsers respond to the subtle influences linked with faults will prove valuable. Now that the Munich group of investigators have developed protocols that yield good, repeatable results, the way is open for other groups to carry out similar research, with the aim of unambiguously showing which fault-linked influences – magnetic changes, microseisms and so on – particular dowsers respond to on specific occasions.

But to fully comprehend the recently recognized energy flows and their geopsychological effects, traditional scientific concepts may well prove insufficient. Newer, more holistic ideas may be needed – updated concepts of *ch'i* or *pneuma*. This is not to open the door to the irrational excesses of New Age thought. But to achieve breakthroughs in understanding, scientists may have to put their thinking caps on and start using new paradigms.

One promising line of attack may lie in the study of self-organizing systems, originally pioneered in particular by Ilya Prigogine and his colleagues at the University of Brussels. If driven far from equilibrium, many highly complex non-living systems – for example certain mixtures of chemicals – spontaneously organize and structure themselves in a manner reminiscent of living things.

In such cases the whole certainly behaves as if it were more than the sum of its parts and the distinction between life and non-life becomes somewhat blurred. As energy flows through Earth's crust, atmosphere and biosphere in complex ways, many such self-organizing systems are likely to form. To take one example, stress in the crust is typically released in the form of innumerable small stick-slip movements along fault planes; these seem to group themselves into self-organizing systems that control the nature and timing of earthquakes.[14] Other examples of such systems might be light balls; their existence as independent units, sometimes displaying complex, even purposive, behaviour hinting that they are not merely self-organized, but perhaps in a sense almost alive. The most complex and mysterious self-organizing systems supported by Earth's energy flows are conscious human brains – in other words ourselves.[15]

If purely physical phenomena such as earthquakes show self-organized, holistic behaviour that defies traditional reductionist analysis, it is perhaps not surprising that more complex geopsychological phenomena have proved difficult for orthodox scientists to understand. Andrei Apostol, the Romanian-born dowser and geophysicist mentioned several times in this book, is developing ideas that he thinks may explain how one self-organizing system – a dowser – interacts with another such system – a stressed fault or other subsurface feature – and thereby detects it.[16]

I personally think that when dealing with dowsing alone such explanations are needlessly complex. A dowser's response to a hidden fault can be simply explained by the supersensory theory without the need to invoke holistic theories. It is when faced with the challenge presented by high-energy fault-linked processes such as poltergeist episodes or the electromagnetic interaction of light balls with human brains that holistic ideas are perhaps needed.

Moreover, such thinking may have to incorporate new insights into the relation between mind and matter. In this regard, David Bohm, FRS, a follower of Einstein renowned for his contributions to quantum theory, has contributed some helpful ideas.[17, 18] Forced to acknowledge the mind-like properties of subatomic particles such as electrons, as revealed by quantum experiments, Bohm contends that everything in the universe has both mental and physical aspects.

Bohm further argues that droplets of mind-matter are not merely parts of the whole as nuts and bolts are parts of a machine, they actually *partake* of the whole. Not only is a whole – for instance, the whole Earth – more than the sum of its parts as in conventional holism, it is in some sense enfolded into each part. So all things on Earth, whether they be pebbles or human beings, partake of the collective Earth mind, as well as the physical body of the planet.

Why such mind-like properties are evident in electrons and humans but not pebbles is a problem remaining to be solved. It may be that relatively large entities need to be, or to incorporate, complex self-organizing systems of a certain kind for mind to reveal itself. If so, perhaps the reason why phenomena such as light balls seem to have mind-like aspects is that, like our brains, they provide stable environments for complex, self-organizing patterns of electromagnetic activity to take place. Of course, lacking the computer-like hard wiring of the human brain, the mental activity of light balls would be completely different from ours – perhaps more electron-like than animal-like. But then, their elusive, observer-dependent behaviour *does* resemble that of those subatomic particles which obstinately defy our efforts to pin them down.

The validity of such revolutionary, superholistic, ways of viewing our relationship with the Earth and its possible mind or minds is for the future to decide. In the meantime our new understanding of previously unrecognized energy flows in Earth's crust and atmosphere can perhaps help us answer the question that has preoccupied so many dowsers in recent years. Did ancient people really locate sites of sacred wells and monuments such as stone circles, henges and barrows at places where *ch'i*-like fluids or 'dowsable Earth energies' emerge from the ground? And if so, why?

Let us first look at holy springs or wells. Because flowing groundwater is often channelled by faults, fracture zones and fissure systems, many ancient wells and holy springs are associated with these geological structures. The famous oracular spring at Delphi in Greece is fed by a fissure system, as are several others.

In Britain, the renowned sacred springs at Bath are related to faulting in a complex way. The water now flowing from the King's Spring, the principal spring in Bath, is fossil water that fell as rain or snow on the nearby limestone Mendip Hills thousands of years ago.[19] Millions of years before that, ancient Earth forces squeezed the local rock layers into a huge fold, so that the fissured limestone beneath the Mendip Hills carries the water about two kilometres underground before conducting it towards the surface again, beneath the city of Bath. As the water slowly travels through the hot, fissured limestone, the water picks up not only heat, but also radioactive elements such as radium-226 and its daughter, radon-222. Finally, geologists believe, the hot, radon-rich water rises rapidly first along a major thrust-fault in the limestone and then via a system of smaller faults to the surface.

Another English holy well located on a fault is the one at Burton Dassett in Warwickshire. The neighbouring twelfth-century Burton Dassett church, probably on a far more ancient sacred site, appeared to be the focus of an outbreak of mysterious lights in the 1920s.[20]

The link of such springs and wells with faults and related geological structures leaves little doubt that many holy springs are located at places where good dowsers or geophysical instruments can detect what some people call 'dowsable Earth energies'. So did the ancients use dowsing to help find these sources of water? As the literature of classical antiquity nowhere mentions the use of the forked twig to locate water or minerals, there is no certain evidence on this point. But it is conceivable that the illiterate Neolithic or Bronze Age inhabitants of Europe used dowsing for this purpose thousands of years before the art was rediscovered by German miners in the late Middle Ages.

Whether or not the ancients actually used forked twigs to locate holy springs of this kind, once shrines were established there, devotees would certainly have been exposed to the subtle influences or 'dowsable Earth energies' associated with faults and fissures. Acting together, high-energy radiation of various kinds from radon and its daughters and ionized air capable of inducing the serotonin stimulation syndrome, may have complex, mind-altering and trance-inducing effects. Could such influences have affected the brain processes of the entranced priestess at Delphi, as she mumbled her prophecies after inhaling vapours from the fissure?

Even more exciting is the possibility that the other kind of fault-linked Earth energies – the sudden, high-energy outbursts that now seem to play a part in light ball and perhaps even poltergeist phenomena – may have enhanced the reputations of certain sacred springs. For instance, it is possible that visitors to these places occasionally witnessed light ball phenomena of the kind seen near the Mochras Fault in 1905 and at Burton Dassett in the 1920s. Just as the God-fearing folk of North Wales saw the lights as signs of divine approval for Mary Jones and her religious movement, the peoples of Neolithic and Early Bronze Age times may have viewed such fault-linked displays as manifestations of the power and majesty of their Great Goddess. It is even conceivable that an occasional witness may have been close enough to an electromagnetically active light ball to experience temporal lobe effects of a religious or mystical nature. Such an experience might well be interpreted as an epiphany of the Goddess herself and could lay the foundations for a whole new cult associated with the spring.

So our growing understanding of fault-linked 'dowsable Earth energies' and their effects on the human brain may throw fresh light on the significance of sacred springs and wells in ancient and non-Western cultures. But what of other ancient sacred sites, such as stone circles, henges and barrows? If they, too, could be shown to be linked with geological faults, exactly the same reasoning would apply, and the concept of dowsable Earth energies would have a much broader explanatory power.

We have already noted Dr J. Havelock Fidler's claim that cairns and standing stones in the Applecross peninsula of Scotland are much closer to faults than might be expected by chance. Other people, notably Paul Devereux and his collaborators, have made similar claims.[21]

Some stone circles are certainly close to faults. The impressive King's Men circle of limestone blocks, on Jurassic limestones at Rollright, Oxfordshire, is near a small fault. The Brackenhall Green and Baildon Moor circles, on the Carboniferous sandstone Rombalds Moor, north of Shipley in Yorkshire are close to local faults that determine the course of the Airedale valley. The circle of forty-one low, boulder-like stones at Moel Ty Uchaf in Clwyd, Wales, on a small plateau of folded Silurian rocks is only a short distance south of the great Bala Fault, along which the River Dee has carved out its valley.[22]

But even if these examples are typical and prehistoric peoples did construct their stone circles and other monuments somewhat closer to geological faults than might be expected by chance, it would be premature to invoke the effects of fault-linked 'dowsable Earth energies'. Because faults often control topography, which in turn influenced the ancient peoples' choice of sacred site, we would expect a correlation of some kind. The point is that stone circles and related monuments are not actually located on faults and fissure systems in the way that many holy springs or wells are. On the contrary, inasmuch as faults tend to be expressed topographically as valleys, whereas prehistoric people typically constructed their stone circles or other monuments on areas of high ground with commanding views, it is likely that relatively few such monuments are actually located on faults or fracture zones. It therefore seems improbable that our fault-linked 'dowsable Earth energies' played much part in ancient peoples' choice of site for stone circles, barrows, henges and the like.

If this is so, what then of the widespread claims by dowsers that they can detect 'Earth energies' at ancient sites of this kind? How can we explain the reports that people *have* seen strange lights near some of these circles? For instance, on 24 July 1984 a woman and her son saw a bright red object, apparently consisting of a cluster of four or five spheres, move across Baildon Moor, passing close to the two stone circles in Yorkshire mentioned above.[23] In 1976, three members of a team of the Royal Observer Corps saw a bright light travel over the same moor and appear to hover over a third stone circle there, near Ilkley.[24] There are many other reports of this kind.

Until recently we would have had to agree with the sceptics that dowsers' reactions at stone circle sites are merely unconscious responses to the obvious visual cues there. The lights would have to remain an unexplained mystery. But in 1991 a new, exciting possibility emerged. Dr Terence Meaden published a book, *The Goddess of the Stones*[25] looking at the stone circles and barrows of the British Isles from a completely fresh viewpoint. Meaden's book throws an entirely new light on the dowsing evidence and the reports of mysterious lights.

Meaden's central argument is an obvious one. For many years, certain hilly areas of Britain, particularly Wessex, have played host to dozens of crop circles. Excluding the proliferating hoaxes, these circles were apparently caused by the descent of those remarkable Meaden vortices that sometimes evolve into electromagnetically active ball-of-light phenomena. The same regions of Britain are riddled with ancient circular monuments: circles of stone or wood and round barrows.

You do not need much imagination to see a possible connection and start speculating. For instance, perhaps the Neolithic and Early Bronze Age inhabitants of Britain observed similar circles in their crops and were so impressed – possibly overwhelmed with feelings of religious awe – that they were moved to commemorate these beautiful but transient effects in the form of permanent replicas of wood or stone.

While it is easy enough to muse along such lines, it is far more difficult to assemble and present evidence good enough to convince orthodox scientists that such an outrageous proposition could possibly be true. Meaden has attempted to do just that. Perhaps his most convincing argument, oddly enough, stems from his demonstration that many of the recent crop circles are not truly circular. According to Meaden, they are often actually ellipses, egg shapes or flattened circles.

We can understand how these precise geometrical shapes may have been generated if we note that only a vertical, stationary, vortex tube descending on a flat, horizontal crop surface would leave a perfectly circular trace in crops. Oblique, moving vortex tubes impinging on sloping, even curved crop surfaces would create not just imperfect circles but a variety of more complex, but still well-defined, geometrical shapes. After making thousands of measurements, Meaden has concluded that many of the recent crop circles have geometries of precisely this kind.

So here we have an elegant geometrical test for Meaden's theory that some of the prehistoric circles and barrows are actually ancient crop circles. If stone circles were all either perfectly circular, or simply crudely marked out circles, the conventional archaeological interpretations would hold good. But if some of them were precise ellipses, egg shapes and so on, Meaden's bizarre interpretation would have strong support indeed.

The evidence seems to provide unequivocal support for Meaden's ideas. In 1967, long before crop circles had attracted publicity, Professor Alexander Thom had measured the dimensions of 211 ancient stone circles with puzzling results.[26] Thom had found that some of the stone circles were not true circles, but ellipses, egg shapes, flattened circles and the like. He had concluded that to create such precise geometrical forms, the megalith builders must have possessed a profound knowledge of geometry, including Pythagoras' theorem.

As it appears incredible that the illiterate Neolithic and Bronze Age inhabitants of Britain could have discovered the principles of geometry thousands of years before Euclid and Pythagoras, few professional archaeologists have supported Thom's conclusion. However, they have not themselves come up with any sensible alternative explanation for the stone circle shapes. Meaden's theory that the prehistoric people merely traced out Nature's own geometrical figures seems to resolve this archaeological conundrum in the most elegant manner.

Several other pieces of evidence support Meaden's claim that at least some of the ancient stone circles and barrows are actually fossilized crop circles, preserved by prehistoric people for their own purposes. For instance, excavations have shown that buried beneath many of the earth barrows are circles of stone or wood, in some cases showing just the same elliptical or other shapes that characterize the exposed stone circles. Why would ancient people bother to mark out such precise shapes and then cover them up were they not commemorating some important event that had occurred there?

Meaden has put forward other arguments to back up the notion that many stone circles and barrows – perhaps even Stonehenge itself – actually correspond to the traces left behind when vortices descended to the ground and damaged crops or other vegetation thousands of years ago. Why prehistoric peoples commemorated circles in this way may never be known. It is possible that they noticed luminous vortices at night in places where they later found crop circles, and attributed both to the awesome powers of the Great Goddess or another deity. It is even conceivable that the rare individual was approached closely enough by an electromagnetically active vortex to experience temporal lobe effects of a religious or mystical nature. Such experiences would certainly have reinforced any existing religious beliefs linked with circles and vortices.

Whatever were the precise reasons that may have led the ancient inhabitants of Britain to locate some of their stone circles and other monuments at crop circle sites, the implications for Earth energy studies and dowsing are potentially revolutionary. For it now seems that some stone circles may be located at what dowsers call Earth energy sites after all. But instead of being places where subtle Earth energies rise along faults, they are locations where energetic, electromagnetically active atmospheric vortices once descended to the ground. Luminous at night, such vortices still seem to appear near these sites today, giving rise to sightings such as those near the Yorkshire stone circles mentioned earlier on.

Could Meaden's theory then explain why so many dowsers experience strong responses at Stonehenge, Rollright, and many other circle sites? Are late twentieth-century dowsers detecting traces of the same spiralling energy displays that prompted the ancient Goddess-worshipping inhabitants of Britain to build their remarkable monuments?

To answer these challenging questions, careful controlled dowsing experiments are needed, along the lines pioneered by the Munich group of investigators. But the very fact that they can be seriously asked is a testament to the new understanding of dowsing that has developed in recent years. For whatever the answer to this particular puzzle, the notion that dowsers can respond to subtle, often fault-linked influences by unconsciously using their Sphinxlike supersenses is now solid enough to take its place in the company of other scientific ideas. Equipped at last with a viable theory, dowsing could soon emerge from the scientific quarantine it entered during the Age of Reason.

Useful Addresses

British Geological Survey
Keyworth
Nottingham
NG12 5GG

National Radiological Protection Board
Chilton
Didcot
Oxfordshire
OX11 0RQ

Deutsche Gesellschaft für Technische Zusammenarbeit (GTZ)
    GmbH
Postfach 5180
D-6236
Eschborn
Germany

British Society of Dowsers
Sycamore Cottage
Tamley Lane
Hastingleigh
Ashford
Kent
TN25 5HW

Chapter References

Introduction

1. Vogt, E.Z. and Hyman, R., *Water Witching USA*, Second Edition, (University of Chicago Press, 1979)

1 The Ancient Art

1. Barrett, Sir William and Besterman, T. *The Divining Rod* (Methuen, 1926)
2. Agricola, G., *De Re Metallica*. Translated from the first Latin edition of 1556 by H.C. Hoover and L.H. Hoover (*Mining* magazine, London, 1912)
3. Boyle, The Hon. Robert, *Certain Physiological Essays* (London, 1661)
4. Locke, J., *Some Considerations on the Consequences of the Lowering of Interest* (London, 1692)
5. Pryce, W., *Mineralogia Cornubiensis: A Treatise on Minerals, Mines, and Mining*, (James Phillips, London, 1778)
6. Ibid.
7. Vallemont, Abbé de (Pierre Le Lorrain) (1693) *La Physique Occulte, ou, Traité de la Baguette Divinatoire*, Paris
8. Barrett and Besterman, op. cit.
9. Bird, C., *The Divining Hand* (E.P. Dutton, New York, 1979)
10. Bird, op. cit.
11. Kircher, A., *Magnes sive de Arte Magnetica* (Cologne, 1643)
12. Bird, op. cit.
13. Boyle, op. cit.
14. de Vallemont, op. cit.
15. Hooson, W., *The Miners' Dictionary* (Wrexham, 1747)
16. Le Brun, P., *Histoire Critique des Practiques Superstitieuses, qui ont seduit le Peuple et Embarassé les Scavans* (Rouen, 1702)
17. Thouvenel, P., *Mémoire Physique et Medicinal montrant des Rapports Evidents entre les Phénomènes de la Baguette Divinatoire, du Magnétisme Animale et de l'Electricité* (Paris, 1781)
18. Thouvenel, P., *Second Mémoire Physique et Medicinal* (Paris, 1784)
19. Matveev, V.S., 'O Biofizicheskom Metode v Geologii' (*Izvestia Akademii Nauk Kazakhskoi SSR*, No.3, 76–84, 1967)
20. Williamson, T. 'Dowsing achieves new credence' (*New Scientist, 81,* 371–373, 1979)
21. Sochevanov, N.N. and Matveev, V.S., 'Biofizicheskii Metod v Geologicheskikh Issledovaniakh' (*Geologia Rudnykh Mestorozhdenii*, No. 5, 77–85, 1974)
22. Stoici, S., Apostol, A., Svoronos, D. and Andreiscu, G., 'On geological, geophysical, geochemical and biogeophysical information in Baia area, Bihor Mountains, Romania' (*Institutul de Geologie si Geofizica, Bucharest, Tectonica si*

Geologie Regionala, 66 115–122 (in Romanian) 1981)
23. Shmidt, N.G., Eremeev, A.N., and Gorelov, D.A., 'Sushchestvuet li Biofizicheskii Metod Poiskov Rudnykh Mestorozhdenii' (*Geologia Rudnykh Mestorozhdenii*, No. 5, 88–96, 1975)

2   The Water Finders

1. Varvill, W.W., 'Geophysical prospecting and dowsing – a mining engineer's experiences' (*Journal of the British Society of Dowsers*, 16, 344–357, 1962)
2. Bertereau, Martine de (1632) *Véritable Déclaration de la Descouverte des Mines et Minières de France* (1632)
3. Galien, C., *La Descouverte des Eaux Minérales de Château-Thierry et de leurs Propriétés* (Paris, 1630)
4. Gobet, N., *Les Anciens Minéralogistes du Royaume de France*, 2 vols (Paris, 1779)
5. Bertereau, Martine de, *La Restitution de Pluton* (1640)
6. Gobet, op. cit.
7. Bird, C., *The Divining Hand*, (E.P. Dutton, New York, 1979)
8. Thouvenel, P., *Mémoire Physique et Medicinal montrant des Rapports Evidents entre les Phénomènes de la Baguette Divinatoire, du Magnétisme Animale et de l'Electricité* (Paris, 1781)
9. Thouvenel, P., *Second Mémoire Physique et Medicinal* (Paris, 1784)
10. Lalande, J.J., 'Lettre sur la Baguette Divinatoire de Bléton', (*Journal des Scavans*, Paris, 1782)
11. Chevreul, M.E., *De la Baguette Divinatoire et du Pendule dit Explorateur* (Mallet-Bachelier, Paris, 1854)
12. Rocard, Y., *La Science et Les Sourciers* (Dunod, Paris, 1989)
13. Barrett, Sir William and Besterman, T., *The Divining Rod* (Methuen, 1926)
14. Rawcliffe, D.H., *The Psychology of the Occult* (Ridgway, 1952)
15. Barrett and Besterman, op. cit.
16. Ibid.
17. Mullins, J. and Mullins, H.W., *The Divining Rod: Its History, Truthfulness and Practical Utility* (J. and H.W. Mullins, Bath, 1908)
18. Pissin, R., 'Dowsing and Reichenbach's Od' (*Journal of the British Society of Dowsers*, 16, 221–228, 1961). Translated from *Zeitschrift für Radiästhesie*, 1960
19. Ibid.
20. Rawcliffe, op. cit.
21. Williamson, A.C., 'Dowsing in East Africa' (*Journal of the British Society of Dowsers*, 17, 167–180, 1963)
22. Schleberger, E., *Drinking Water Supply and Sanitation Project in Sri Lanka* (Schriftenreihe der Deutschen Gesellschaft für Technische Zusammenarbeit (GTZ) No. 183, Eschborn, Germany, 1986)
23. Betz, H.-D., *Unkonventionelle Wasserfindung* (English translation in preparation.) (*Deutsche Gesellschaft für Technische Zusammenarbeit (GTZ)*, Eschborn, Germany, 1991)
24. Betz, H.-D., *Geheimnis Wünschelrüte* (Umschau Verlag, Frankfurt, 1990)
25. Betz, 1991, op. cit.
26. Betz, 1990, op. cit.
27. Betz, 1991, op. cit.

3   Dowsing, Earth Rays and Cancer

1. Pohl, G.F. von, *Earth Currents: Causative Factor of Cancer and Other Diseases* (Translation of 1932 original by Ingrid Lang) (Frech-Verlag, Stuttgart, 1987)
2. Bird, C., *The Divining Hand* (E.P. Dutton, New York, 1979)
3. Bell, A.H., 'Earth Rays', (*Journal of the British Society of Dowsers*, 19, 154–163, 1964)
4. Bird, op. cit.
5. Maes, W., 'Radioaktivität über Wasseradern – Teil 1'' (*Wohnung und*

Gesundheit, No. 55, 27–29, 1990)

6. National Radiological Protection Board, *Gamma-radiation Levels Outdoors in Great Britain*, NRPB-R191 (HMSO, 1988)

7. National Radiological Protection Board, *Radiation Exposure of the UK population – 1988 Review*, NRPB-R227 (HMSO, 1989)

8. Maes, W., 'Radioaktivität über Wasseradern – Teil 2'' (*Wohnung und Gesundheit*, No. 56, 24–26, 1990)

9. von Pohl, op. cit.

10. Ibid.

11. Pearce, F., 'A deadly gas under the floorboards' (*New Scientist*, 5 February, 33–35, 1987)

12. Ibid.

13. National Radiological Protection Board (1988) *Natural Radiation Exposure in UK Dwellings*, NRPB-R190 (HMSO, 1988)

14. Harding, C., Interview with Alan Franks (*The Times*, 20 February 1990)

15. Department of the Environment, 'The Householder's Guide to Radon' (Leaflet D62NJ, London, 1988)

16. Durrance, E., 'Radon: an unobtrusive geological hazard' (*British Geologist*, 13, 72–76, 1987)

17. Bird, op. cit.

18. Apostol, A., Mihail, C., Spinoche, S., Malnasi, G., 'O posibila relatie intre elemente de structura geologica si distributia teritoriala a unor forme de cancer' (*VII Simpozion de Prospectiuni Geofizice*, Bucharest, 1972)

19. Agricola, G., *De Re Metallica*. Translated from the first Latin edition of 1556 by H.C. Hoover and L.H. Hoover (*Mining* magazine, London, 1912)

4   A New Technique for Archaeologists

1. Bird, C., *The Divining Hand* (E.P. Dutton, New York, 1979)

2. Ibid.

3. Viré, A., *Comment Devenir Sourcier, Ce Que J'ai Vu, Ce Que J'ai Fait*, Librairie J-B Bailliere (Paris, 1948)

4. Rocard, Y., *La Science et Les Sourciers* (Dunod, Paris, 1989)

5. Bird, op. cit.

6. Bailey, R.N., 'Dowsing for mediaeval churches' (*Popular Archaeology*, 4, 33–37, 1983)

7. Briggs, H.D., Cambridge, E. and Bailey, R.N., 'A new approach to church archaeology: dowsing, excavation and documentary work at Woodhorn, Ponteland and the pre-Norman Cathedral at Durham' (*Archaeologia Aeliana* ser. 5, 11, 79–100, 1983)

8. Briggs, H.D. Cambridge, E. and Bailey, R.N., 'A new approach to church archaeology, II: dowsing and excavations at Ponteland and St. Oswald's, Durham' (*Archaeologia Aeliana* ser. 5, 13, 133–146, 1985)

9. Bailey, R.N., Cambridge, E. and Briggs, H.D., *Dowsing and Church Archaeology*, Intercept, Wimborne, Dorset, 1988)

10. Ibid.

11. Nevin, C. (1990) 'The past and the paranormal' (*The Times Saturday Review*, October 6, 10–12, 1990)

5   The Sceptics Refuted

1. Ellis, A.J., *The Divining Rod: A History of Water Witching*, (U.S. Geological Survey Water-Supply Paper 416, Government Printing Office, Washington D.C., 1917)

2. Hansen. G.P., 'CSICOP and the Skeptics: An Overview' (*Journal of the American Society for Psychical Research*, 86, 19–63, 1992)

3. Randi, J., 'Help Stamp Out Absurd Beliefs' (*Time* magazine, 13 April, 80, 1992)

4. Rawcliffe, D.H., *The Psychology of the Occult* (Ridgway, 1952)

5. Betz, H.-D., *Geheimnis Wünschelrüte*, (Umschau Verlag, Frankfurt, 1990)
6. Betz, H.-D., *Unkonventionelle Wasserfindung*, (Deutsche Gesellschaft für Technische Zusammenarbeit (GTZ), Eschborn, 1991.) (English translation in preparation.)
7. Popper, K., *The Logic of Scientific Discovery* (Hutchinson, 1959)
8. Vogt, E.Z. and Hyman, R., *Water Witching USA*, Second Edition (University of Chicago Press, 1979)
9. Ibid.
10. Dale, L.A. et al., 'Dowsing: a field experiment in water divining' (*Journal of the American Society for Psychical Research*, 45, 3–16, 1951)
11. König, H.L. and Betz, H.-D., *Erdstrahlen? Der Wünschelruten-Report*, H.L. König und H.-D. Betz, München (1989)
12. Foulkes, R.A., 'Dowsing experiments' (*Nature*, 229, 163–168, 1971)
13. McAnulla, R.J., 'Weak Magnetic Fields and the Dowser's Reflex' (M. Phil. Thesis, City University, London, 1970)
14. McAnulla, R.J., 'The Location of Underground Objects using Dowsing Rods' (Report No. ECRC/M337, Electricity Council Research Centre, Capenhurst, 1971)
15. Chadwick, D.G., and Jensen, L., 'The Detection of Magnetic Fields Caused by Groundwater and the Correlation of Such Fields with Water Dowsing' (Utah Water Research Laboratory, College of Engineering, Utah State University, PRWG 78–1, 1971)
16. Betz, 1991, op. cit.
17. Ibid.
18. König and Betz, op. cit.
19. Betz, 1990, op. cit.
20. Apostol, A. (1991) Personal communication to author
21. König and Betz, op. cit.

6   *The Riddle of the Sphinx*

1. Tromp, S.W., *Psychical Physics* (Elsevier, Amsterdam, 1949)
2. Tromp, S.W., *Experiments On the Possible Relationship between Soil Resistivity and Dowsing Zones* (Oegstgeest, Leiden, 1954)
3. Tromp, S.W., 'Review of the possible physiological causes of dowsing' (*International Journal of Parapsychology*, 10, 363–391, 1968)
4. Tromp, S.W., 'Water divining (dowsing)' in Fairbridge (Ed.) (*The Encyclopedia of Geochemistry and the Environmental Sciences*, Van Nostrand Reinhold, New York, 1972)
5. Vogt, E.Z. and Hyman, R., *Water Witching USA*, Second Edition (University of Chicago Press, 1979)
6. Ibid.
7. Jung, C.G., *Civilization in Transition* (Routledge and Kegan Paul, London, 1964)

7   *When the Snakes Awake*

1. Downer, J., *Supersense* (BBC Books, 1988)
2. Redgrove, P., *The Black Goddess and the Sixth Sense* (Bloomsbury, 1987)
3. Tromp, S.W., 'Water divining (dowsing)' in Fairbridge (Ed.) *The Encyclopedia of Geochemistry and the Environmental Sciences*, Van Nostrand Reinhold, New York, 1972)
4. Rawcliffe, D.H., *The Psychology of the Occult* (Ridgway, 1952)
5. Downer, op. cit.
6. Tributsch, H., *When the Snakes Awake* (The MIT Press, Cambridge, Massachusetts, USA, 1982)
7. Brownell, P.H., 'Prey detection by the sand scorpion' (*Scientific American*, 251, 94–105, 1984)
8. Wüst, J., 'Microseismic and the dowsing problem' (*Journal of the British*

Society of Dowsers, 17, 374–382, 1963) Translated from *Zeitschrift für Radiästhesie*, 2, (1951)
9. König, H.L. and Betz, H.-D. (1989) *Erdstrahlen? Der Wünschelruten-Report* (H.L. König und H.-D. Betz, München, 1989)
10. Wüst, op. cit.

8 Our Magnetic Supersense

1. Klinowska, M., 'No through road for the misguided whale' (*New Scientist*, 113, 46–48, 1987)
2. MacKenzie, D., 'Whales (and scientists) left high and dry' (*New Scientist*, 6 November, 24, 1986)
3. Klinowska, op. cit.
4. Klinowska, M., 'Geomagnetic orientation in cetaceans: behavioural evidence', *Sensory Abilities of Cetaceans*, ed. J. Thomas and R. Kastelein (Plenum, New York, 651–663, 1990)
5. Kirschvink, J.L., Dizon, A.E., and Westphal, J.A., 'Evidence from strandings for geomagnetic sensitivity in cetaceans' (*Journal of Experimental Biology*, 120, 1–24, 1986)
6. Kirschvink, J.L., 'Geomagnetic orientation in cetaceans: an update with live stranding records in the USA', *Sensory Abilities of Cetaceans*, ed. J. Thomas and R. Kastelein (Plenum, New York, 639–649, 1990)
7. Blakemore, R.P., 'Magnetotactic bacteria' (*Science* 190, 377–379, 1975)
8. Walker, M.M., 'Learned magnetic field discrimination in yellowfin tuna, *Thunnus albacares*' (*Journal of Comparative Physiology*, 155, 673–679, 1984)
9. Gould, J.L., 'The map sense of pigeons' (*Nature*, 296, 205–211, 1982)
10. Mather, J.G. and Baker, R.R., 'Magnetic sense of direction in woodmice for route-based navigation' (*Nature*, 291, 152–155, 1981)
11. Baker, R.R., *Human navigation and the sixth sense* (Hodder & Stoughton, 1981)
12. Baker, R.R., 'Goal orientation by blindfolded humans after long-distance displacement: possible involvement of a magnetic sense' (*Science*, 210, 555–557, 1980)
13. Baker, R.R., 'A sense of magnetism' (*New Scientist*, 87, 844–846, 1980)
14. Baker, 1981, op. cit.
15. Baker, R.R., 'Human navigation and magnetoreception: the Manchester experiments do replicate' (*Animal Behaviour*, 35, 691–704, 1987)
16. Ibid.
17. Young, S., 'The mini explorers of Middle Earth' (*New Scientist*, 30 September, 38–42, 1989)
18. Blakemore, R.P. and Frankel, R.B., 'Magnetic navigation in bacteria' (*Scientific American*, 245, 58–65, 1981)
19. Walker, M.M., Kirschvink, J.L., Chang, S-B.R. and Dizon, A.E., 'A candidate magnetic sense organ in the yellowfin tuna, *Thunnus albacares*' (*Science*, 224, 751–753, 1984)
20. Kirschvink, 1990, op. cit.
21. Baker, R.R., Mather, J.G., and Kennaugh, J.H., 'Magnetic bones in human sinuses' (*Nature*, 301, 78–80, 1983)
22. Maugh, T.H., 'Caltech scientists find magnetic particles in human brains' (*Los Angeles Times*, 5 May, A1, 1992)
23. Barinag, M., 'Giving personal magnetism a whole new meaning' (*Science*, 256, 96, 1992)
24. Kirschvink, J.L. et. al., 'Proceedings of the National Academy of Sciences' (in press).
25. Leask, M.J.M., 'A physicochemical mechanism for magnetic field detection by migratory birds and homing pigeons' (*Nature*, 267, 144–145, 1977)
26. Semm, P., Nohr, D., Demaine, C. and Wiltschko, W., 'Neural basis of the

magnetic compass: interactions of visual, magnetic and vestibular inputs in the pigeon's brain' (*Journal of Comparative Physiology, A*, 155, 283–288, 1984)

27. Semm, P. and Demaine, C., 'Neurophysiological properties of magnetic cells in the pigeon's visual system' (*Journal of Comparative Physiology, A*, 159, 619–625, 1986)

28. Schulten, K., 'Magnetic field effects in chemistry and biology', *Advances in Solid State Physics XXII* (Vieweg, Braunschweig, 61–83, 1982)

29. Schulten, K. and Windemuth, A., 'Model for a physiological magnetic compass', *Biological Effects of Static Magnetic Fields* ed. Maret, G., Kiepenhauer, J. and Boccara, N. (Springer, Berlin, 99–106, 1986)

30. Cremer-Bartels, G., Krause, K., Mitoskas, G., and Brodersen, D., 'Magnetic field of the Earth as additional zeitgeber for endogenous rhythms?' (*Naturwissenschaften*, 71, 567–574, 1984)

31. Cremer-Bartels, G., Krause, K. and Küchle, H.J., 'Influence of low magnetic-field-strength variations on the retina and pineal gland of quails and humans' (*Graefe's Archive for Clinical and Experimental Ophthalmology*, 220, 248–252, 1983)

9 The Electromagnetic Link

1. Maby, J.C. and Franklin, T.B., *The Physics of the Divining Rod* (Bell, 1939)

2. Franklin, T.B., *Radiations* (Bell, 1949)

3. Wever, R., 'Effects of electric fields on circadian rhythms in men', *Life Sciences and Space Research, VIII* North-Holland, 1970)

4. Persinger, M.A., 'Geopsychology and geopsychopathology: Mental processes and disorders associated with geophysical and geochemical factors' (*Experientia*, 43, 92–104, 1987)

5. Ruhenstroth-Bauer, G., Baumer, H., Kugler, J., Spatz, R., Sönning, W., and Filipiak, B., 'Epilepsy and weather: a significant correlation between the onset of epileptic seizures and specific atmospherics – a pilot study.' (*International Journal of Biometeorology*, 28, 333–340, 1984)

6. Ruhenstroth-Bauer, G. Baumer, H., Burkel, E.M., Sönning, W. and Filipiak, B., 'Myocardial infarction and the weather: a significant correlation between the onset of heart infarct and 28 kHz atmospherics – a pilot study' (*Clinical Cardiology*, 8, 149–151, 1985)

7. Ruhenstroth-Bauer, G., Mees, K., Sandhagen, R., Baumer, H., and Filipiak, B., 'Demonstration of statistical significance correlations between 8 and 12 kHz atmospherics and sudden deafness' (*Zeitschrift für Naturforschung*, 42c, 999–1000, 1987

8. Brown, F.A., 'An orientational response to weak gamma variation' (*Biological Bulletin*, 125, 206, 1963)

9. Tributsch, H., *When the Snakes Awake* (The MIT Press, Cambridge, Massachusetts, USA, 1982)

10. Hopwood, A., 'Dowsing, ley lines and the electromagnetic link' (*New Scientist*, 20–27 December, 948–949, 1979)

11. Kracmar, F., 'Concerning the biophysics of radiesthesia', (*Supplement to Journal of the British Society of Dowsers*, 114, 1961). Translated from *Erfahrungsheilkunde*, 10, Part 1–2, 1961.

12. Tromp, S.W., *Experiments On the Possible Relationship between Soil Resistivity and Dowsing Zones* (Oegstgeest, Leiden, 1954)

13. Baker, R.R. 'Human navigation and magnetoreception: the Manchester experiments do replicate' (*Animal Behaviour*, 35, 691–704, 1987)

14. Williamson, T., 'A sense of direction for dowsers?' (*New Scientist*, 113, 40–43, 1987)

10 Dowsing Explained?

1. Rocard, Y., *Les Sourciers* (Presses Universitaires de France, Paris, 1981)

2. Tromp, S.W., *Psychical Physics* (Elsevier, Amsterdam, 1949)

3. Tromp, S.W., *Experiments On the Possible Relationship between Soil Resistivity and Dowsing Zones* (Oegstgeest, Leiden, 1954)

4. Tromp, S.W., 'Water divining (dowsing)' in Fairbridge (ed.) *The Encyclopedia of Geochemistry and the Environmental Sciences* (Van Nostrand Reinhold, New York, 1972)

5. Rocard, Y., (*Le Signal du Sourcier*, Dunod, Paris, 1962)

6. Chadwick, D.G. and Jensen, L., 'The Detection of Magnetic Fields Caused by Groundwater and the Correlation of Such Fields with Water Dowsing' (Utah Water Research Laboratory, College of Engineering, Utah State University, PRWG 78–1, 1971)

7. Rocard, 1981, op. cit.

8. Betz, H.-D., *Unkonventionelle Wasserfindung* (*Deutsche Gesellschaft für Technische Zusammenarbeit (GTZ)*, Eschborn, 1991, (English translation in preparation.)

9. König, H.L. and Betz, H.-D., *Erdstrahlen? Der Wünschelruten-Report* (H.L. König und H.-D. Betz, München, 1989)

10. Ibid.

11. Ibid.

12. Simmons, G., 'Cooperation between geophysics and dowsing' (*American Dowser*, 24, 6–11, 1984)

13. Bird, C., (*The Divining Hand*, E.P. Dutton, New York, 1979

14. Williamson, A.C., 'Dowsing in East Africa' (*Journal of the British Society of Dowsers*, 17, 167–180, 1963)

15. Barca, R.A., Personal communication to author, 1991

16. Sochevanov, N.N. and Matveev, V.S., 'Biofizicheskii Metod v Geologicheskikh Issledovaniakh' (*Geologia Rudnykh Mestorozhdenii*, No. 5, 1974)

17. Aitken, M.J., *Physics and Archaeology* (Clarendon Press, Oxford, 1974)

18. Woodhouse, M., 'Locating wells using dowsing and earth conductivity in Kenya' (*Journal of the British Society of Dowsers*, 35, 16–21, 1992)

11   Earth Energies

1. Watkins, A., *The Old Straight Track* (Methuen, 1925)

2. Williamson, T. and Bellamy, L., *Ley Lines in Question* (World's Work, 1983)

3. Graves, T., *The Diviner's Handbook* (Aquarian Press, Wellingborough, Northamptonshire, 1986)

4. Graves, T., *Needles of Stone Revisited* (Gothic Image, Glastonbury, 1988)

5. Graves, R., *The Greek Myths*, 2 vols, Penguin Books, 1960)

6. Devereux, P., *Places of Power* (Blandford Press, 1990)

7. Ibid.

8. Underwood, G., *The Patterns of the Past* (Abacus, 1972)

9. Fidler, J.H., *Earth Energy* (Aquarian Press, Wellingborough, Northamptonshire, 1988)

10. Tributsch, H., *When the Snakes Awake*, The MIT Press, Cambridge, Massachusetts, USA, 1982)

11. Ibid.

12. Ouellet, M. (1990) 'Earthquake lights and seismicity' (*Nature*, 348, 492, 1990)

13. Tributsch, op. cit.

14. Lovelock, J., *Gaia: A New Look at Life on Earth*, Oxford University Press, 1982)

15. Lovelock, J., *The Ages of Gaia* (Oxford University Press, 1988)

16. Tributsch, op. cit.

17. Johnston, M.J.S., 'Review of magnetic and electric field effects near active faults and volcanoes in the USA' (*Physics of the Earth and Planetary Interiors*, 57, 47–63, 1989)

18. Fujinawa, Y. and Takahashi, K., 'Emission of electromagnetic radiation preceding the Ito seismic swarm of 1989' (*Nature*, 347, 376–378, 1990)

19. Wüst, J., 'Microseismic and the dowsing problem' (*Journal of the British*

Society of Dowsers, 17, 374–382, 1963). Translated from *Zeitschrift für Radiästhesie*, 2, (1951).

20. Apostol, A., Molnar-Veress, M. and Svoronos, D., 'Preliminary data on precursor phenomena of intermediate-depth earthquakes in Vrancea seismic region of Romania' (*Researches in Geophysics*, 19, 31–39, Institute of Geology and Geophysics, Bucharest, 1981 [in Romanian])

21. Pryce, W., *Mineralogia Cornubiensis: A Treatise on Minerals, Mines, and Mining* (James Phillips, 1778)

22. Devereux, P., *Earth Lights Revelation* (Blandford Press, 1989)

23. Ibid.

24. Ibid.

25. Ibid.

26. Wiedemann, C.L., 'Results of the New Jersey 'spook light' study' (*Vestigia Newsletter*, 2, 1–4, 1977)

27. Devereux, 1989, op. cit.

28. Persinger, M.A. and Derr, J.S., 'Geophysical variables and behavior: XXIII: Relations between UFO reports within the Uinta basin and local seismicity' (*Perceptual and Motor Skills*, 60, 143–152, 1985)

29. Derr, J.S. and Persinger, M.A., 'Luminous phenomena and earthquakes in southern Washington' (*Experientia*, 42, 991–999, 1986)

30. Persinger, M.A. and Derr, J.S., 'Geophysical variables and behavior: XXII: Evaluations of UFO reports in an area of infrequent seismicity: the Carman, Manitoba episode' (*Perceptual and Motor Skills* 61, 807–813, 1985)

31. Zoback, M.L., Zoback, M.D., Adams, J., Assumpcao, M., Bell, S., Bergman, E.A., Blümling, P., Brereton, N.R., Denham, D., Ding, J., Fuchs, K., Gay, N., Gregerson, S., Gupta, H.K., Gvishiani, A., Jakob, K., Klein, R., Knoll, P., Magee, M., Mercier, J.L., Müller, B.C., Paquin, C., Rajendran, K., Stephansson, O., Suarez, G., Suter, M., Udias, A., Xu, Z.H., and Zhizhin, M., 'Global patterns of tectonic stress' (*Nature*, 341, 291–298, 1989)

32. Yamada, I., Masuda, K. and Mizutani, H., 'Electromagnetic and acoustic emission associated with rock fracture' (*Physics of the Earth and Planetary Interiors*, 57, 157–168, 1989)

33. Wiedemann, op. cit.

34. Ohtsuki, Y.H. and Ofuruton, H., 'Plasma fireballs formed by microwave interference in air' (*Nature*, 350, 139–141, 1991)

35. Derr and Persinger, op. cit.

36. Tributsch, op. cit.

12   Dowsing and the Crop Circles Mystery

1. Noyes, R. (ed.) *The Crop Circle Enigma*, Gateway Books, Bath, 1990

2. Green, M., 'The rings of time: the symbolism of the crop circles' (*The Crop Circle Enigma* (ed. Noyes), Gateway Books, Bath, 137–171, 1990)

3. Meaden, G.T., *The Circles Effect and its Mysteries*, Artetech, Bradford-on-Avon.

4. Meaden, G.T., 'Circles from the sky – a new topic in atmospheric research' 'Proceedings of the First International Conference on the Circles Effect' (ed. D.M. Elsom), Oxford Polytechnic, 11–52, 1990.

5. Randles, J. and Fuller, P., *Crop Circles – A Mystery Solved*, (Robert Hale, 1990)

6. Fuller, P., Meaden, G.T. and Randles, J., 'A response to the claims by Bower and Chorley' (*The Crop Watcher*, No. 7, 4–8, 1991)

7. Meaden, G.T., 'Crop circles and the plasma vortex', *The Crop Circle Enigma* (ed. Noyes) (Gateway Books, Bath, 76–97, 1990)

8. Girvan, W. 'The Wiltshire crater mystery' (*Flying Saucer Review*, 9, 3–7, 1963)

9. Williamson, T., 'The Charlton crater' (*Flying Saucer Review*, 9, 26–27, 1963)

10. Girvan, op. cit.

11. *Dorset Evening Echo,* July 27 1963
12. Shuttlewood, A., *The Warminster Mystery* (N. Spearman, 1967)
13. Ibid.
14. Ibid.
15. Meaden, 1989, op. cit.
16. Ibid.
17. Randles and Fuller, op. cit.
18. Ibid.
19. Meaden, G.T., 'Nocturnal eyewitness observation of circles in the making, Part 2: North Wiltshire, 29 June 1989' (*Journal of Meteorology,* 15, 5–7, 1990)
20. Meaden, 1989, op. cit.
21. Ibid.
22. Meaden, G.T., 'Observation of a circle in process of formation, near Dundee, Scotland, after dawn in late August 1989' 'Proceedings of the First International Conference on the Circles Effect' (ed. D.M. Elsom), Oxford Polytechnic, 122–124, 1990
23. Meaden, 1989, op. cit.
24. Singer, S., 'Great balls of fire' (*Nature,* 350, 108–109, 1991)
25. Devereux, 1989, op. cit.
26. Rowe, M.W. and Meaden, G.T., 'A case of ball lightning inside a bedroom in Greater Manchester' (*Journal of Meteorology,* 15, 157–158, 1990)
27. Meaden, G.T. 'Spontaneous combustion – an eyewitness case from Hungary' (*Journal of Meteorology,* 15, 320, 1990)
28. Meaden, 1989, op. cit.
29. Ohtsuki, Y.H. and Ofuruton, H., 'Plasma fireballs formed by microwave interference in air' (*Nature,* 350, 139–141, 1991)
30. Meaden, 1989, op. cit.
31. Ibid.

13 Geopsychology

1. Ouellet, M., 'Earthquake lights and seismicity' (*Nature,* 348, 492, 1990)
2. Persinger, M.A. and Cameron, R.A. 'Are Earth faults at fault in some poltergeist-like episodes?' (*Journal of the American Society for Psychical Research,* 80, 49–73, 1986)
3. Randles, J. and Fuller, P. *Crop Circles – A Mystery Solved* (Robert Hale, 1990)
4. Spencer, J., *UFOs – The Definitive Casebook* (Hamlyn, 1991)
5. Randles and Fuller, op. cit.
6. Persinger, M.A., 'Geophysical variables and behavior: IX. 'Expected clinical consequences of close proximity to UFO-related luminosities' (*Perceptual and Motor Skills,* 56, 259–265, 1983)
7. Ruhenstroth-Bauer, G., Baumer, H., Kugler, J., Spatz, R., Sönning, W., and Filipiak, B. (1984) 'Epilepsy and weather: a significant correlation between the onset of epileptic seizures and specific atmospherics – a pilot study' (*International Journal of Biometeorology,* 28, 333–340, 1984)
8. Michaud, L.Y. and Persinger, M.A., 'Geophysical variables and behavior: XXV. 'Alterations in memory for a narrative following application of theta frequency electromagnetic fields' (*Perceptual and Motor Skills,* 60, 416–418, 1985
9. Ruttan, L.A., Persinger, M.A. and Koren, S., 'Enhancement of temporal lobe-related experiences during brief exposures to milligauss intensity extremely low frequency magnetic fields' (*Journal of Bioelectricity,* 9, 33–54, 1990)
10. Devereux, P., *Earth Lights* (Turnstone Press, Wellingborough, Northamptonshire, 1982)
11. Lovell, J.H., 'Symposium on a technique for earthquake prediction and monitoring in situ stress' (*British Geologist,* 14, 16, 1988)
12. Yamada, I., Masuda, K. and Mizutani, H., 'Electromagnetic and acoustic emission associated with rock fracture' (*Physics of the Earth and Planetary Interiors,*

57, 157–168, 1989)

13. Persinger, M.A., 'Geophysical variables and behavior: LIII. Epidemiological considerations for incidence of cancer and depression in areas of frequent UFO reports' (*Perceptual and Motor Skills*, 67, 799–803, 1988)

14. Scholz, C.H., 'Earthquakes as chaos', (*Nature*, 348, 197–198, 1990)

15. Freeman, W.J., 'The physiology of perception' (*Scientific American*, February, 34–41, 1991)

16. Apostol, A., Personal communication to author, 1991.

17. Bohm, D., *Wholeness and the Implicate Order* (Routledge and Kegan Paul, 1980)

18. Bohm, D., 'Toward a new theory of the relationship of mind and matter', *Frontier Perspectives*, 1, 9–25, Temple University, Philadelphia, 1990.

19. Andrews, J.N., Burgess, W.G., Edmunds, W.M., Kay, R.L.F., and Lee, D.J. 'The thermal springs of Bath' (*Nature*, 298, 339–343, 1982)

20. Devereux, P., *Earth Lights Revelation* (Blandford Press, 1989)

21. Devereux, P., *Earth Memory* (Quantum, 1991)

22. Devereux, P., *Places of Power* (Blandford Press, 1990)

23. Ibid.

24. Ibid.

25. Meaden, G.T., *The Goddess of the Stones* (Souvenir Press, 1991)

26. Thom, A., *Megalithic Sites in Britain* (Clarendon Press, 1967)

References and Bibliography

Agricola, G., *De Re Metallica*. Translated from the first Latin edition of 1556 by H.C. Hoover and L.H. Hoover (Mining Magazine, 1912)

Aitken, M.J., *Physics and Archaeology*, (Clarendon Press, 1974)

Andrews, J.N., Burgess, W.G., Edmunds, W.M., Kay, R.L.F. & Lee, D.J., 'The thermal springs of Bath' (*Nature*, 298, 339–343, 1982)

Apostol, A., Mihail, C., Spinoche, S. and Malnasi, G. (1972) 'O posibila relatie intre elemente de structura geologica si distributia teritoriala a unor forme de cancer' (*VII Simpozion de Prospectiuni Geofizice*, Bucharest, 1972)

Apostol, A., Molnar-Veress, M. and Svoronos, D., 'Preliminary data on precursor phenomena of intermediate-depth earthquakes in Vrancea seismic region of Romania', *Researches in Geophysics*, 19, 31–39, 1981. Institute of Geology and Geophysics, Bucharest (in Romanian).

Bailey, R.N., 'Dowsing for mediaeval churches' (*Popular Archaeology*, 4, 33–37, 1983)

Bailey, R.N., Cambridge, E. and Briggs, H.D., *Dowsing and Church Archaeology* (Intercept, 1988)

Baker, R.R., 'Goal orientation by blindfolded humans after long-distance displacement: possible involvement of a magnetic sense' (*Science*, 210, 555–557, 1980)

Baker, R.R., 'A sense of magnetism' (*New Scientist*, 87, 844–846, 1980)

Baker, R.R., *Human navigation and the sixth sense* (Hodder & Stoughton, 1981)

Baker, R.R., 'Human navigation and magnetoreception: the Manchester experiments do replicate' (*Animal Behaviour*, 35, 691–704, 1987)

Baker, R.R., Mather, J.G., and Kennaugh, J.H., 'Magnetic bones in human sinuses' (*Nature*, 301, 78–80, 1983)

Bakirov, A.G., Malakhov, A.A., Matveev, V.S. and Sochevanov, N.N., 'Da, Biofizicheskii Metod Sushchestvuet!' (*Geologia Rudnykh Mestorozhdenii*, No. 4, 116–120, 1976)

Balanovski, E. and Taylor, J.G., 'Can electromagnetism account for extra-sensory phenomena?' (*Nature*, 276, 64–67, 1978)

Barinag, M., 'Giving personal magnetism a whole new meaning' (*Science*, 256, 96, 1992)

Barrett, Sir William and Besterman, T., *The Divining Rod* (Methuen, 1926) London

Bell, A.H., 'Earth Rays' (*Journal of the British Society of Dowsers*, 19, 154–163, 1964)

Bertereau, Martine de, *Véritable Déclaration de la Descouverte des Mines et*

Minières de France (1632)

Bertereau, Martine de, *La Restitution de Pluton* (1640)

Betz, H.-D., *Geheimnis Wünschelrüte* (Umschau Verlag, Frankfurt, 1990)

Betz, H.-D., *Unkonventionelle Wasserfindung* (Deutsche Gesellschaft für Technische Zusammenarbeit (GTZ), Eschborn, Germany, 1991) (English translation in preparation.)

Bird, C., *The Divining Hand* (E.P. Dutton, New York, 1979)

Blakemore, R.P., 'Magnetotactic bacteria' (*Science*, 190, 377–379, 1975)

Blakemore, R.P. and Frankel, R.B., 'Magnetic navigation in bacteria', (*Scientific American*, 245, 58–65, 1981)

Bohm, D., *Wholeness and the Implicate Order* (Routledge and Kegan Paul, 1980)

Bohm, D., 'Toward a new theory of the relationship of mind and matter', *Frontier Perspectives*, 1, 9–25 (Temple University, Philadelphia, 1990)

Boyle, The Hon. Robert, *Certain Physiological Essays* (London, 1661)

Briggs, H.D., Cambridge, E. and Bailey, R.N., 'A new approach to church archaeology: dowsing, excavation and documentary work at Woodhorn, Ponteland and the pre-Norman Cathedral at Durham' (*Archaeologia Aeliana* ser. 5, 11, 79–100, 1983)

Briggs, H.D., Cambridge, E. and Bailey, R.N., 'A new approach to church archaeology, II: dowsing and excavations at Ponteland and St. Oswald's, Durham' (*Archaeologia Aeliana* ser. 5, 13, 133–146, 1985)

Brown, F.A., 'An orientational response to weak gamma variation' (*Biological Bulletin*, 125, 206, 1963)

Brownell, P.H., 'Prey detection by the sand scorpion' (*Scientific American*, 251, 94–105, 1984)

Chadwick, D.G., and Jensen, L., 'The Detection of Magnetic Fields Caused by Groundwater and the Correlation of Such Fields with Water Dowsing', 'Utah Water Research Laboratory, College of Engineering, Utah State University, PRWG 78–1, 1971

Chevreul, M.E., *De la Baguette Divinatoire et du Pendule dit Explorateur* (Mallet-Bachelier, Paris, 1854)

Comunetti, A.M., 'Systematic experiments to establish the spatial distribution of the physiologically effective stimuli of unidentified nature' (*Experientia*, 34, S.889–893, 1978)

Comunetti, A.M., 'Experimental investigation of the perceptibility of the artificial source for the dowsing agent' (*Experientia*, 35, S.420–424, 1979)

Cremer-Bartels, G., Krause, K. and Küchle, H.J., 'Influence of low magnetic-field-strength variations on the retina and pineal gland of quails and humans' (*Graefe's Archive for Clinical and Experimental Ophthalmology*, 220, 248–252, 1983)

Cremer-Bartels, G., Krause, K., Mitoskas, G. and Brodersen, D., 'Magnetic field of the Earth as additional zeitgeber for endogenous rhythms?' (*Naturwissenschaften*, 71, 567–574, 1984)

Dale, L.A. et al., 'Dowsing: a field experiment in water divining', (*Journal of the American Society for Psychical Research*, 45, 3–16, 1951

Department of the Environment, 'The Householder's Guide to Radon' Leaflet D62NJ, 1988

Derr, J.S. and Persinger, M.A., 'Luminous phenomena and earthquakes in southern Washington' (*Experientia*, 42, 991–999, 1986)

Devereux, P.. and Thomson, I., *The Ley Hunter's Companion* (Thames & Hudson, 1979)

Devereux, P., *Earth Lights* (Turnstone Press, 1982)

Devereux, P., *Earth Lights Revelation* (Blandford Press, 1989)

Devereux, P., *Places of Power* (Blandford Press, 1990)

Devereux, P., *Earth Memory* (Quantum, 1991)

Downer, J., *Supersense* (BBC Books, 1988)

Durrance, E., 'Radon: an unobtrusive geological hazard' (*British Geologist*, 13, 72–76, 1987)

Ellis, A.J., 'The Divining Rod: A History of Water Witching', U.S. Geological Survey Water-Supply Paper 416, Government Printing Office, Washington D.C., 1917

Fidler, J.H., *Earth Energy* (Aquarian Press, 1988)

Foulkes, R.A., 'Dowsing experiments' (*Nature*, 229, 163–168, 1971)

Franklin, T.B., *Radiations* (Bell, 1949)

Freeman, W.J., 'The physiology of perception' (*Scientific American*, February, 34–41, 1991)

Fujinawa, Y. and Takahashi, K., 'Emission of electromagnetic radiation preceding the Ito seismic swarm of 1989' (*Nature* 347, 376–378, 1990)

Fuller, P., Meaden, G.T. and Randles, J., 'A response to the claims by Bower and Chorley' (*The Crop Watcher*, No. 7, 4–8, 1991)

Galien, C., *La Descouverte des Eaux Minérales de Château-Thierry et de leurs Propriétés* (Paris, 1630)

Girvan, W., 'The Wiltshire crater mystery' (*Flying Saucer Review*, 9, 3–7, 1963)

Gobet, N., *Les Anciens Minéralogistes du Royaume de France*, 2 vols (Paris, 1779)

Gould, J.L., 'The map sense of pigeons' (*Nature*, 296, 205–211, 1982)

Graves, R., *The Greek Myths*, 2 vols (Penguin Books, 1960)

Graves, T., *The Diviner's Handbook* (Aquarian Press, 1986)

Graves, T., *Needles of Stone Revisited* (Gothic Image, 1988)

Green, M., 'The rings of time: the symbolism of the crop circles', *The Crop Circle Enigma* (ed. Noyes) (Gateway Books, 137–171, 1990)

Hansen, G.P., 'Dowsing: a review of experimental research' (*Journal of the American Society for Psychical Research*, 51, 343–367, 1982)

Hansen, G.P., 'CSICOP and the Skeptics: An Overview' (*Journal of the American Society for Psychical Research*, 86, 19–63, 1992)

Harding, C., Interview with Alan Franks, *The Times*, 20 February 1990

Hooson, W. (1747) *The Miners' Dictionary* (Wrexham, 1747)

Hopwood, A. (1979) 'Dowsing, ley lines and the electromagnetic link' (*New Scientist* 20–27 December, 948–949, 1979)

Irons, F.E., 'Concerning the non-linear behaviour of the forced pendulum including the dowsing pendulum' (*European Journal of Physics*, 11, 107–115, 1990)

Johnston, M.J.S., 'Review of magnetic and electric field effects near active faults and volcanoes in the USA' (*Physics of the Earth and Planetary Interiors*, 57, 47–63, 1989)

Jung, C.G., *Civilization in Transition* (Routledge and Kegan Paul, 1964)

Kircher, A., *Magnes sive de Arte Magnetica* (Cologne, 1643)

Kirschvink, J.L., 'Geomagnetic orientation in cetaceans: an update with live stranding records in the USA', *Sensory Abilities of Cetaceans*, ed. J. Thomas and R. Kastelein (Plenum, New York, 639–649, 1990)

Kirschvink, J.L., Dizon, A.E., and Westphal, J.A., 'Evidence from strandings for geomagnetic sensitivity in cetaceans' (*Journal of Experimental Biology*, 120, 1–24, 1986)

Kirschvink, J.L. et al. *Proceedings of the National Academy of Sciences*. (in press) 1992

Klinckowstroem, Count Carl von, 'The problem of the divining rod' (*Scientific American*, 149, 218–219, 1933)

Klinowska, M., 'No through road for the misguided whale' (*New Scientist*, 113, 46–48, 1987)

Klinowska, M., 'Geomagnetic orientation in cetaceans: behavioural evidence', *Sensory Abilities of Cetaceans*, ed. J. Thomas and R. Kastelein, (Plenum, New York, 651–663, 1990)

König, H.L. and Betz, H.-D., *Erdstrahlen? Der Wünschelruten-Report* (H.L. König und H.-D. Betz, München, 1989)

Kracmar, F., 'Concerning the biophysics of radiesthesia', (*Supplement to Journal of the British Society of Dowsers*, 114, 1961). Translated from *Erfahrungsheilkunde*, 10, Part 1-2, 1961

Lalande, J.J., 'Lettre sur la Baguette Divinatoire de Bléton', (*Journal des Scavans*, Paris, 1782)

Leask, M.J.M., 'A physicochemical mechanism for magnetic field detection by migratory birds and homing pigeons', *Nature*, 267, 144–145, 1977)

Le Brun, P., *Histoire Critique des Practiques Superstitieuses, qui ont seduit le Peuple et Embarassé les Scavans* (Rouen, 1702)

Locke, J., *Some Considerations on the Consequences of the Lowering of Interest* (London, 1692)

Lovell, J.H., 'Symposium on a technique for earthquake prediction and monitoring in situ stress' (*British Geologist*, 14, 16, 1988)

Lovelock, J., *Gaia: A New Look at Life on Earth* (Oxford University Press, 1982)

Lovelock, J., *The Ages of Gaia* (Oxford University Press, 1988)

Maby, J.C. and Franklin, T.B., *The Physics of the Divining Rod* (Bell, 1939)

MacKenzie, D., 'Whales (and scientists) left high and dry' (*New Scientist*, 6 November, 24, 1986)

Maes, W., 'Radioaktivität über Wasseradern – Teil 1' (*Wohnung und Gesundheit*, Nr. 55, 27–29, 1990)

Maes, W., 'Radioaktivität über Wasseradern – Teil 2' (*Wohnung und Gesundheit*, Nr. 56, 24–26, 1990)

Mather, J.G. and Baker, R.R., 'Magnetic sense of direction in woodmice for route-based navigation' (*Nature*, 291, 152–155, 1981)

Matveev, V.S., 'O Biofizicheskom Metode v Geologii' (*Izvestia Akademii Nauk Kazakhskoi SSR*, No. 3, 76–84 1967)

Maugh, T.H., 'Caltech scientists find magnetic particles in human brains' (*Los Angeles Times*, 5 May 1992, A1)

McAnulla, R.J., 'Weak Magnetic Fields and the Dowser's Reflex' M.Phil. Thesis, City University, 1970

McAnulla, R.J., 'The Location of Underground Objects using Dowsing Rods', Report No. ECRC/M337, Electricity Council Research Centre, Capenhurst, 1971

Meaden, G.T., *The Circles Effect and its Mysteries* (Artetech, 1989)

Meaden, G.T., 'Circles from the sky – a new topic in atmospheric research', 'Proceedings of the First International Conference on the Circles Effect' (ed. D.M. Elsom), Oxford Polytechnic, 11–52, 1990

Meaden, G.T., 'Crop circles and the plasma vortex', *The Crop Circle Enigma*, (ed. Noyes) (Gateway Books, 76–97, 1990)

Meaden, G.T., 'Nocturnal eyewitness observation of circles in the making, Part 2: North Wiltshire, 29 June 1989' (*Journal of Meteorology*, 15, 5–7, 1990)

Meaden, G.T., 'Observation of a circle in process of formation, near Dundee, Scotland, after dawn in late August 1989', 'Proceedings of the First International Conference on the Circles Effect' (ed. D.M. Elsom), Oxford Polytechnic, 122–124, 1990

Meaden, G.T., 'Spontaneous combustion – an eyewitness case from Hungary' (*Journal of Meteorology*, 15, 320, 1990)

Meaden, G.T., *The Goddess of the Stones*, Souvenir Press, 1991

Michaud, L.Y. and Persinger, M.A., 'Geophysical variables and behavior: XXV. 'Alterations in memory for a narrative following application of theta frequency electromagnetic fields' (*Perceptual and Motor Skills*, 60, 416–418, 1985)

Mullins, J., Mullins, H.W., *The Divining Rod: Its History, Truthfulness and Practical Utility* (J. and H.W. Mullins, Bath, 1908)

National Radiological Protection Board, 'Natural Radiation Exposure in UK Dwellings', NRPB-R190, Her Majesty's Stationery Office, 1988

National Radiological Protection Board, 'Gamma-radiation Levels Outdoors in Great Britain', NRPB-R191, Her Majesty's Stationery Office, 1988

National Radiological Protection Board, 'Radiation Exposure of the UK population – 1988 Review', NRPB-R227, Her Majesty's Stationery Office, 1989

Nevin, C., 'The past and the paranormal' (*The Times Saturday Review*, October 6, 10–12, 1990)

Noyes, R., (ed.) *The Crop Circle Enigma* (Gateway Books, 1990)

Ohtsuki, Y.H. and Ofuruton, H., 'Plasma fireballs formed by microwave interference in air', (*Nature*, 350, 139–141, 1991)

Ouellet, M., 'Earthquake lights and seismicity', (*Nature*, 348, 492, 1990)

Parsons, D., 'A dampener for the dowsers' (*The Independent*, 19 September 1988)

Pearce, F., 'A deadly gas under the floorboards' (*New Scientist*, 5 February, 1987, 33–35)

Persinger, M.A., 'Geophysical variables and behavior: IX. 'Expected clinical consequences of close proximity to UFO-related luminosities' (*Perceptual and Motor Skills*, 56, 259–265, 1983)

Persinger, M.A., 'Geophysical variables and behavior: XXII. 'The tectonogenic strain continuum of unusual events' (*Perceptual and Motor Skills*, 60, 59–65, 1985)

Persinger, M.A., 'Geophysical variables and behavior: XXIX. Intense paranormal experiences occur during days of quiet, global geomagnetic activity' (*Perceptual and Motor Skills*, 61, 320–322, 1985)

Persinger, M.A., 'Geopsychology and geopsychopathology: Mental processes and disorders associated with geophysical and geochemical factors' (*Experientia*, 43, 92–104)

Persinger, M.A., 'Geophysical variables and behavior: LIII. Epidemiological considerations for incidence of cancer and depression in areas of frequent UFO reports' (*Perceptual and Motor Skills*, 67, 799–803, 1988)

Persinger, M.A., 'Increased geomagnetic activity and the occurrence of bereavement hallucinations: evidence for melatonin-mediated microseizuring in the temporal lobe?' (*Neuroscience Letters*, 68, 271–274, 1988)

Persinger, M.A., 'Geophysical variables and behavior: LV. Predicting the details of visitor experiences and the personality of experients: the temporal lobe factor' (*Perceptual and Motor Skills*, 68, 55–65, 1989)

Persinger, M.A. and Cameron, R.A., 'Are Earth faults at fault in some poltergeist-like episodes?' (*Journal of the American Society for Psychical Research*, 80, 49–73, 1986)

Persinger, M.A. and Derr, J.S., 'Geophysical variables and behavior: XXIII: Relations between UFO reports within the Uinta basin and local seismicity' (*Perceptual and Motor Skills*, 60, 143–152, 1985)

Persinger, M.A. and Derr, J.S., 'Geophysical variables and behavior: XXII: Evaluations of UFO reports in an area of infrequent seismicity: the Carman, Manitoba episode' (*Perceptual and Motor Skills*, 61, 807–813, 1985)

Pissin, R., 'Dowsing and Reichenbach's Od' (*Journal of the British Society of Dowsers*, 16, 221–228, 1961) Translated from *Zeitschrift für Radiästhesie*, 1960.

Pohl, G.F. von, *Earth Currents: Causative Factor of Cancer and Other Diseases* (Frech-Verlag, Stuttgart, 1987) (Translation of 1932 original by Ingrid Lang).

Popper, K., *The Logic of Scientific Discovery* (Hutchinson, 1959)

Pryce, W., *Mineralogia Cornubiensis: A Treatise on Minerals, Mines, and Mining* (James Phillips, 1778)

Randi, J., 'A controlled test of dowsing abilities' (*The Skeptical Inquirer*, 4, 16–20, 1979)

Randi, J., *Flim-Flam! Psychics, ESP, Unicorns and Other Delusions* (Prometheus, Buffalo, New York, 1982)

Randi, J., 'Help stamp out absurd beliefs' (*Time Magazine*, 13 April, 80, 1992)

Randles, J. and Fuller, P., *Crop Circles – A Mystery Solved* (Robert Hale, 1990)

Rawcliffe, D.H., *The Psychology of the Occult* (Ridgway, 1952)

Redgrove, P., *The Black Goddess and the Sixth Sense* (Bloomsbury, 1987)

Rocard, Y., *Le Signal du Sourcier* (Dunod, 1962)

Rocard, Y., 'Actions of a very weak magnetic gradient: the reflex of the dowser' in: *Biological Effects of Magnetic Fields*, ed. M.F. Barnothy (Plenum, New York, 279–286, 1964)

Rocard, Y., 'Le Signal du Sourcier' (*La Recherche*, 12, 792–799, 1981)

Rocard, Y., *Les Sourciers* (Presses Universitaires de France, Paris, 1981)

Rocard, Y., *La Science et Les Sourciers* (Dunod, Paris, 1989)

Rössler, B. *Speculum Metallurgiae Politissimum* (Dresden, 1700)

Rowe, M.W., and Meaden, G.T., 'A case of ball lightning inside a bedroom in Greater Manchester' (*Journal of Meteorology*, 15, 157–158, 1990)

Ruhenstroth-Bauer, G., Baumer, H., Kugler, J., Spatz, R., Sönning, W., and Filipiak, B., 'Epilepsy and weather: a significant correlation between the onset of epileptic seizures and specific atmospherics – a pilot study.' (*International Journal of Biometeorology*, 28, 333–340, 1984)

Ruhenstroth-Bauer, G., Baumer, H., Burkel, E.M., Sönning, W. and Filipiak, B., 'Myocardial infarction and the weather: a significant correlation between the onset of heart infarct and 28 kHz atmospherics – a pilot study' (*Clinical Cardiology*, 8, 149–151, 1985)

Ruhenstroth-Bauer, G., Rösing, O. and Baumer, H., 'Correlation between the 8- and 10-kHz atmospherics and the inflammation reaction of rats' (*Naturwissenschaften*, 73, S625-626, 1986)

Ruhenstroth-Bauer, G., Mees, K., Sandhagen, R., Baumer, H., and Filipiak, B., 'Demonstration of statistical significance correlations between 8 and 12 kHz atmospherics and sudden deafness' (*Zeitschrift für Naturforschung*, 42c, 999–1000, 1987)

Ruhenstroth-Bauer, G., Rüther, E., and Reinertshofer, Th. 'Dependence of a sleeping parameter from the N-S or E-W sleeping direction' (*Zeitschrift für Naturforschung*, 42c, 1140–1142, 1987)

Ruttan, L.A., Persinger, M.A. and Koren, S., 'Enhancement temporal lobe-related experiences during brief exposures to milligauss intensity extremely low frequency magnetic fields' (*Journal of Bioelectricity*, 9, 33–54, 1990)

Schleberger, E., 'Drinking Water Supply and Sanitation Project in Sri Lanka' (*Schriftenreihe der Deutschen Gesellschaft für Technische Zusammenarbeit (GTZ)* No 183, Eschborn, Germany, 1986)

Scholz, C.H., 'Earthquakes as chaos' (*Nature*, 348, 197–198, 1990)

Schulten, K., 'Magnetic field effects in chemistry and biology', in *Advances in Solid State Physics XXII* (Vieweg, Braunschweig, 61–83, 1982)

Schulten, K. and Windemuth, A., 'Model for a physiological magnetic compass' in : *Biological Effects of Static Magnetic Fields* ed. Maret, G., Kiepenhauer, J. and Boccara, N. (Springer, Berlin, 99–106, 1986)

Semm, P. and Demaine, C., 'Neurophysiological properties of magnetic cells in the pigeon's visual system' (*Journal of Comparative Physiology* A, 159, 619–625, 1986)

Semm, P., Nohr, D., Demaine, C. and Wiltschko, W., 'Neural basis of the magnetic compass: interactions of visual, magnetic and vestibular inputs in the pigeon's brain' (*Journal of Comparative Physiology*, A, 155, 283–288, 1984)

Shmidt, N.G., Eremeev, A.N., and Gorelov, D.A., 'Sushchestvuet li Biofizicheskii Metod Poiskov Rudnykh Mestorozhdenii' (*Geologia Rudnykh Mestorozhdenii*, No. 5, 88–96, 1975)

Shuttlewood, A., *The Warminster Mystery* (N. Spearman, 1967)

Simmons, G., 'Cooperation between geophysics and dowsing' (*American Dowser*, 24, 6–11, 1984)

Singer, S., 'Great balls of fire' (*Nature*, 350, 108–109, 1991)

Smith, C.W. and Best, S., *Electromagnetic Man* (J.M. Dent, 1989)

Sochevanov, N.N. and Matveev, V.S., 'Biofizicheskii Metod v Geologicheskikh Issledovaniakh' (*Geologia Rudnykh Mestoroxhdenii*, No. 5., 77–85, 1974)

Spencer, J., *UFOs – The Definitive Casebook* (Hamlyn, 1991)

Stoici, S., Apostol, A., Svoronos, D. and Andreiscu, G., 'On geological, geophysical, geochemical and biogeophysical information in Baia area, Bihor Mountains, Romania', *Institutul de Geologie si Geofizica, Bucharest, Tectonica si Geologie Regionala*, 66, 115–122, 1981 (in Romanian).

Thom, A., *Megalithic Sites in Britain* (Clarendon Press, 1967)

Thouvenel, P., *Mémoire Physique et Medicinal montrant des Rapports Evidents entre les Phénomènes de la Baguette Divinatoire, du Magnétisme Animale et de l'Electricité (Paris, 1781)*

Thouvenel, P., *Second Mémoire Physique et Medicinal* (Paris, 1784)

Tributsch, H., *When the Snakes Awake* (The MIT Press, Cambridge, Massachusetts, USA, 1982)

Tromp, S.W., *Psychical Physics* (Elsevier, Amsterdam, 1949)

Tromp, S.W., *Experiments On the Possible Relationship between Soil Resistivity and Dowsing Zones*, (Foundation for the Study of Psycho-Physics) Oegstgeest, Leiden, 1954

Tromp, S.W., 'Review of the possible physiological causes of dowsing', (*International Journal of Parapsychology*, 10, 363–391, 1968)

Tromp. S.W., 'Water divining (dowsing)' in Fairbridge (Ed.) *The Encyclopedia of Geochemistry and the Environmental Sciences* (Van Nostrand Reinhold, New York, 1972)

Underwood, G., *The Patterns of the Past* (Abacus, London, 1972)

Vallemont, Abbé de (Pierre Le Lorrain), *La Physique Occulte, ou, Traité de la Baguette Divinatoire* (Paris, 1693)

Varvill, W.W., 'Geophysical prospecting and dowsing – a mining engineer's experiences' (*Journal of the British Society of Dowsers*, 16, 344–357, 1962

Viré, A., *Comment Devenir Sourcier, Ce Que J'ai Vu, Ce Que J'ai Fait* (Librairie J-B Bailliere, Paris, 1948)

Vogt, E.Z. and Hyman, R., *Water Witching USA*, Second Edition (University of Chicago Press, 1979)

Walker, M.M., 'Learned magnetic field discrimination in yellowfin tuna, *Thunnus albacares*' (*Journal of Comparative Physiology*, 155, 673–679, 1984)

Walker, M.M., Kirschvink, J.L., Chang, S-B.R. and Dizon, A.E., 'A candidate magnetic sense organ in the yellowfin tuna, *Thunnus albacares*' *Science*, 224, 751–753, 1964)

Watkins, A., *The Old Straight Track* (Methuen, 1925)

Wever, R., 'Effects of electric fields on circadian rhythms in men', (*Life Sciences and Space Research, VIII*, North-Holland, 1970)

Wiedemann, C.L., 'Results of the New Jersey "spook light" study (*Vestigia Newsletter*, 2, 1–4, 1977)

Williamson, A.C., 'Soil resistivity instruments as an aid to dowsing' (*Journal of the British Society of Dowsers*, 16, 340–342, 1962)

Williamson, A.C., 'Dowsing in East Africa' (*Journal of the British Society of Dowsers*, 17, 167–180, 1963)

Williamson, T., 'The Charlton crater' (*Flying Saucer Review*, 9, 26–27, 1963)

Williamson, T., 'Dowsing achieves new credence' (*New Scientist*, 81, 371–373, 1979)

Williamson, T., 'Dowsing explained' (*Nature*, 320, 569, 1986)

Williamson, T., 'A sense of direction for dowsers?' (*New Scientist*, 113, 40–43, 1987)

Williamson, T. and Bellamy, L., *Ley Lines in Question* (World's Work, 1983)

Woodhouse, M., 'Locating wells using dowsing and earth conductivity in Kenya' (*Journal of the British Society of Dowsers*, 35, 16–21, 1992)

Wüst, J., 'Microseismic and the dowsing problem' (*Journal of the British Society of Dowsers*, 17, 374–382, 1963). Translated from *Zeitschrift für Radiästhesie*, 2, (1951)

Yamada, I., Masuda, K. and Mizutani, H., 'Electromagnetic and acoustic emission associated with rock fracture' (*Physics of the Earth and Planetary Interiors*, 57, 157–168, 1989)

Young, S., 'The mini explorers of Middle Earth' (*New Scientist*, 30 September 1989, 38–42)

Zoback, M.L., Zoback, M.D., Adams, J., Assumpcao, M., Bell, S., Bergman, E.A., Blümling, P., Brereton, N.R., Denham, D., Ding, J., Fuchs, K., Gay, N., Gregerson, S., Gupta, H.K., Gvishiani, A., Jakob, K., Klein, R., Knoll, P., Magee, M., Mercier, J.L., Müller, B.C., Paquin, C., Rajendran, K., Stephansson, O., Suarez, G., Suter, M., Udias, A., Xu, Z.H., and Zhizhin, M. 'Global patterns of tectonic stress' (*Nature*, 341, 291–298, 1989)

Index